Calcu

skills

PAT PERKS

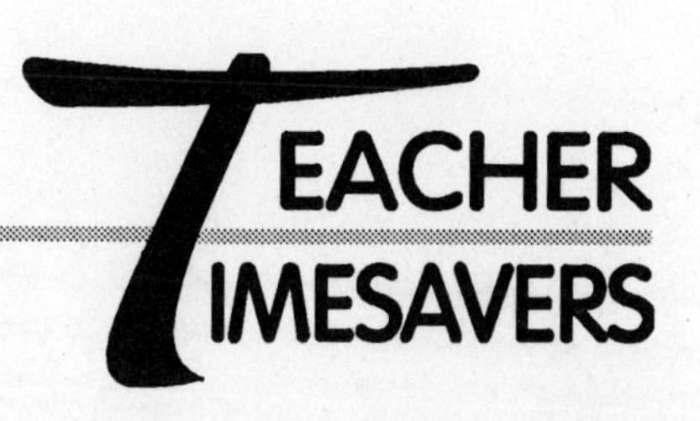

Published by Scholastic Ltd.,
Villiers House,
Clarendon Avenue,
Leamington Spa,
Warwickshire CV32 5PR

Author Pat Perks
Editor Jo Saxelby-Jennings
Assistant editor Joanne Boden
Series designer Joy White
Designer Tracey Ramsey
Illustrations Lorna Kent
Cover illustration Frances Lloyd
Cover photograph Martyn Chillmaid

Designed using Aldus Pagemaker
Printed in Great Britain by Clays Ltd, Bungay, Suffolk

British Library Cataloguing-in-Publication Data
A catalogue record for this book is
available from the British Library.

ISBN 0-590-53344-4

Acknowledgements

The author and publishers wish to thank Oxfam for their help in producing pages 103 and 115 of this book. The division of Oxfam's funds diagram on page 103 is taken from a 1993 Oxfam leaflet, 'Shopping with Oxfam'.

Contents

Introduction

There has been much debate in recent years over the use of calculators in schools, much of it fuelled by the press releases that accompanied the publication of the 1994 Ofsted report *Science and Mathematics in Schools: A review* (London: HMSO). These implied that calculators were being used unnecessarily in schools and that, as a result, children's numeracy was deteriorating. In fact, the Ofsted report quoted the Assessment of Performance Unit in saying that it: 'did not find any evidence that the widespread use of calculators was associated with lower performance'. The report also stated clearly that: 'calculators are not over-used in schools' and, indeed, that the teaching of their proper use is not yet covered sufficiently.

Calculators are a fact of modern life and they offer the learner an exciting opportunity to work on number in an exploratory way. A calculator allows experimentation – wrong results can easily be discarded, patterns can be discovered, hypotheses tested – and it provides a focus for discussions about numbers – correct results can be shared, discoveries can be talked about.

It is true that a child who finds learning number difficult and is introduced to a calculator late, can gain the impression that 'calculators do it better' and may tend to over-rely on their use. However, if they use a calculator as they learn and are encouraged to think about number, its patterns and its forms, they will use their brains first. The sixteen-year-old who reaches for a calculator to double a number is not the pupil who has worked with a calculator creatively.

Let the children in your class play with calculators and while they play they will not only develop a facility for using the calculator but also develop pictures of number relationships which will help them to become better at mental arithmetic. In addition, you will find that many areas of work can be visited much earlier than expected – for example, decimal and negative numbers – and the children come to accept these as numbers to be explored.

Using the activity sheets

Many of the activity sheets have a variety of answers. Do not allow this to pressure you into becoming a marking machine. Instead, encourage the children to justify their solutions. Let them convince you that their answers are correct. Working in groups usually means that the children can become even more creative, their discussions showing how clearly they understand the mathematics.

Some of the activities use, as their data, information on cards. This seems to make working through lots of problems easier for many children. Sorting, matching and discussing are easier if you can move the data around.

Many of the games can (and should) be adapted. Children can also be encouraged to design their own versions. Making up questions is often a better way of learning mathematics than just answering them.

The activities in the 'Across the levels' section have been used over many years with a wide range of ages and abilities. Some activities are suitable for Level 1 children to play with, while children working towards Level 6 can be encouraged to generalise, test, predict and justify. Sometimes the written presentation might be unsuitable for the young learner, but the mathematical ideas are not. Such activities can enable you to differentiate by outcome. The children will be working on the same ideas, but you can observe how their achievements vary.

Do not be put off by the order in which the activities are presented. Some of the later work is quite suitable for younger children and some of the earlier work can be used to reinforce and remind later on: you know the level of strategy and mathematics the children have developed.

Finally, some activities involve using the calculator to record a result, not to calculate. This offers a very important level of security for some children. The answers can 'disappear' quickly if incorrect and answers can be considered several times before they are recorded in a more permanent form. 'Trial-and-improvement' is a very important technique, and children should be encouraged to value their mistakes.

Above all, the activities in this book are designed to give children the opportunity to enjoy using calculators. Encourage this enjoyment and help it to spread to the rest of their mathematics work.

Classroom calculators

Given the range of calculators available, even for the 'primary' market, the activities in this book can only assume a general type. You will find that a number of variations in the keys and sequences of key presses needed for certain operations have been suggested on the activity sheets, for example when finding percentages or using the memory facility. In particular, you should become familiar with the way in which the C, CE or AC keys work and the combinations of memory keys provided on your classroom calculators. The activities in this book assume √, x^2, +/-, % and F ⋛ D keys are present, but your models may only have some (or none) of them.

About the author

Pat Perks is a lecturer in mathematics education in the University of Birmingham School of Education. While working as an advisory teacher for Birmingham LEA, she was involved with a three year programme where calculators were provided for use in Year 1 in all Birmingham infant schools.

Symbols used in teachers' notes

The code given after each activity title in these teachers' notes indicates for which groupings of children the activity is suitable. If there is a 'best' grouping, this is indicated by bold type.
I = individuals, P = pairs, G = small group, C = whole class.
❑ denotes extension ideas.

Towards Level 1

Fill your display (IPGC) This activity introduces children to calculator digits and their formation. At first, you may need an adult to get a group started. Try to give the children odd moments to design their own displays and talk about them. They will need at least two pieces of digital paper each (page 136).
Clear and copy (P) Another activity for practising digits. The children will have to take care to transfer the digits properly. To play, the children choose a trail each and put their counters by their first number. They take turns to copy their first number on to the calculator display. If everyone agrees it is correct, they can move their counter on to the next number. If the number on the calculator does not match the number on the trail, the counter stays where it is until the next time. Then the other player clears the display and enters their first number. The first person to reach the end of their trail is the winner. Give the children opportunities to talk about what they are doing, to check each other's work and to work cooperatively. This activity also reinforces their knowledge of how to clear the display.
Train spotting (I) In this transfer activity, the children copy numbers on to the calculator display and then colour the picture. Any colouring activity could be adapted to do this.
Counting cubes (IPGC) Here the children count and then record in two different ways. Children distinguish easily between repeated digits, patterns and numbers – so do not worry, the style will not confuse them. It is a useful device for you too – a screen of digits is easy to check.
❑ Show the children some cubes, then hide some behind your back, show them how many are left and ask them to fill the screen with the number of cubes behind your back. Also, roll a number word using the units number roller (the net is given on page 131), and then ask them to fill the screen with that digit.
Ship ahoy! (I) In this transfer activity, the children have to distinguish between a 5 and a 2 (sometimes problematic) for a particular colour.
Count and display (IPG) This activity involves using symbols for numbers, counting and recording, and uses the calculator as a recording device. The children will need digital paper (page 136) to record their displays.
❑ Give the children the display of numbers and ask them to put out sets of cubes.
Reversing Rita (IPGC) Most children enjoy the concentration required to do this ordered digits activity, but they will make plenty of (valuable) mistakes. Digital paper (page 136) will be required.
❑ Look at palindromic numbers (that is, numbers which read the same forwards and backwards, for example 1221). Let the children add the number and its reverse – is the answer palindromic? If not, add the reverse of this new number – is the answer palindromic? Continue until a palindromic number is displayed.
Symmetrical shields (IP) This activity is about finding and recognising sets of digits. Using a calculator a number from one shield can be placed near the other shield for comparison. The children should choose a number, enter it on to their calculators and then colour that part of the picture and any other parts on both shields with the same number. Then they should choose another part with a different number, continuing until both shields are completely coloured. What do they notice?
Counting on a calculator (IPGC) This is one of the most useful (and exciting) activities on the calculator. Together, watch the numbers change as the = key is pressed. The children will pick up the keystrokes very quickly and may count to much bigger numbers than you would expect.
❑ There are lots of opportunities for oral work 'on the mat', predicting numbers before or after, 1 less than or 1 more than and so on. Use long strips of paper to record the sets of numbers.
How many? (IG) This activity uses the counting constant to help children to recognise that the last number in the count is the number of objects in the set. The physical connection between pointing and pressing is really valuable.
❑ Use sets of real objects. The recording can be done using pictures and numbers.
Cubes and grids (IP**G**C) This matching activity uses the counting constant, 2cm cubes and number grids (pages 137–139). Try stopping the children and asking them, 'How many cubes are there on your grid?'. There will be some who will look at the calculator, some who will pick up the

last cube and look at the number underneath and some who will count the cubes.
❑ Use lots of different number grids and different stopping numbers. Consider the patterns made on the different grids by different counting constants. Does counting to 20 on a 2 grid look the same as on a 4 grid or a 10 grid? For some children use a smaller copy of the grids for recording, as their transfer skills will be well developed.
Cubes to add (IPGC) The calculator makes it very clear that the + sign really does something! The 1 to 9 number cards (page 140) are needed for this activity.
❑ 0 can be added, as can other number cards.
Constant dots (I) A dot-to-dot picture, based on counting in 1s on the calculator, helps with finding the next number, careful transfer and the process of counting.
Number towers (IPGC) This activity explores number bonds for 7. It shows the children that the + sign does something and develops their recording skills. Most children are able to do this for two towers, but the difficulty is often in encouraging them to write the sum which matches the picture - having written 4, 3 and 7, they feel that no more is needed. Asking them how the 4 and the 3 will give 7 on the calculator display reinforces the role of the + and = signs. Some children will find the transfer to three towers difficult, probably because most of their work has been on combining two sets.
❑ Try four or five towers or a different number of cubes.
Totem totals (IPGC) This sheet provides lots of work on number bonds.
❑ Make totem poles with three spaces, or make up other rules, such as to get the top number double one number and add it to the other.

Towards Level 2

Number hunt (IP) This activity provides opportunities to practise addition, using the calculator as a recording device.
❑ Encourage the children to make up clues to a display of their telephone number or birth date.
Calculator trail (P) This game encourages addition. Listen to the children's different ways of moving between the numbers, for example + 3 or + 1 + 1 + 1. Check that the operations the children choose will take them from 0 to 11 or 12, depending on the trail chosen.
❑ Play the game in reverse for subtraction. At a higher level only, allow multiplication or division either way. You may like to encourage empty box notation, that is 2 + ▯ = 5, to record results.
Addition bonds: 5 to 10 (IPG) Lots more addition practice here. The calculator offers the child speed and confidence in adding up.
❑ The cards can be used to play the game of 'Pairs' (also called 'Pelmanism'), using the calculator to check decisions. Alternatively, use the cards to play a sorting game using the sheet 'House numbers' on page 23 as the game board, or play a card game where each player is dealt four cards and can exchange with the pack in turns until someone has a run of four consecutive answers.
House numbers (IPG) Most young children enjoy making up their own sums to put on the houses.
❑ Draw a three storey house or block of flats for lots more sums. Can the children do a similar activity with subtractions? At a lower level, use the sheet to put the correct number of cubes on to each house.
Skittles (P) This activity practises addition and subtraction. Ask the children which are the easiest skittles to knock down. Encourage them to keep a record of their dice throws.
Where am I going? (IG) More addition and subtraction practice. Can the children design routes through the maze to the other objects?
❑ Play as a game. Generate pairs of numbers with dice or digit spinners. The players can then choose any of the four operations to make new calculations for routes through the maze. Give scores to the various destinations.
Trihexes (IG) Lots of practice in addition and subtraction. The calculator is for speed and to raise the children's confidence. Recording may be easier on hexagon paper.
How old is the tortoise? (I) An activity using addition, subtraction and more than/less than.
❑ Change the colours to obtain more 'exotic' tortoises.
From here to there (IPGC) Encourage the children to work in groups and to be as creative as possible in finding ways to move from one number to the next.
See-saw sums (IPGC) More on number bonds, but working towards 3 + 4 = 2 + 5.
❑ Introduce empty box notation for recording. What does the see-saw look like for:
3 + 4 = ▯ + ▯ = ▯, or 2 + ▯ = 6 = 1 + ▯ and so on?
Triangle totals (IPGC) The children will develop strategies for the task, and some may wish to use decimals or negative numbers. What happens if they use the same number at each vertex (corner)?
❑ Extend the activity to use any polygons.
Magic constant (IPGC) An exciting way of hiding addition and subtraction. It will soon become a regular game, with the children challenging each other.
Answers: 7, 9, 12; 3, 7, 12, 50, 83, 115; 8, different calculators do give different answers here.
❑ Try using multiplication or division to set up constants.

More than, less than (IPG) The calculator is used to find the missing value in a 'more than' or 'less than' number sentence.

❏ Use the 'Pocket money toy cards' (page 141) or the 'Price label cards' (page 142) instead of the number cards.

Three in a row (P) This 'Noughts and crosses'-like game develops mental arithmetic and requires addition and a strategy for winning. Young children have little strategy and play by trial-and-error to begin with, but once they start to see lines of three they will begin to do the calculations mentally to choose the numbers they need. Help them develop such a strategy.

Words to add (IP) This sheet links reading number words and practising addition.

❏ Generate the number words to be added with the units number roller (the net is provided on page 131).

Deal a difference (P) A game for practising difference and the language of 'higher' and 'lower'.

❏ Let the player with the lower number score the points. The children could use the 'Pocket money toy cards' (page 141) or the 'Price label cards' (page 142) instead of the number cards.

Pocket money toys (IPG) This sheet deals with adding money. Encourage the children to be as creative as possible, and to find as many different answers as they can to each question. Using the extra 'Pocket money toy cards' (page 141) means that different children could work on the same questions with different data.

Towards Level 3

Star sums (IPGC) This activity is similar to 'Triangle totals', page 40, but uses five numbers. Encourage the children to be creative in their choice of numbers.

❏ Use money as the centre number and limit the outer numbers to the value of coins.

Magic circle (IP) Lots of addition practice here. The children need to keep track of the numbers. *Answer:* the magic circle total is 65.

Triangle jigsaw (IP) Mental arithmetic is developed putting the jigsaw pieces together. *Answer – for example:*

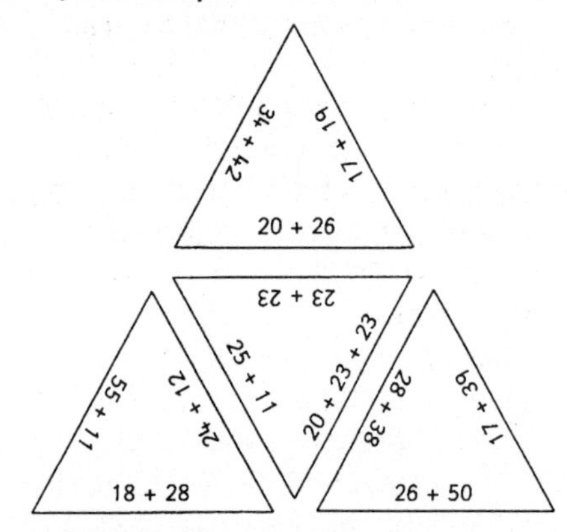

A number flower (IPGC) This sheet offers a way of recording number pairs for a particular number. The children may wish to use decimals or negative numbers.

A 5s dot-to-dot (I) This dot-to-dot picture uses counting-on in 5s, using the calculator to help with finding the next number. This activity reinforces the multiples of 5.

❏ Adapt other dot-to-dot pictures for counting-on in 3s or 4s.

Number maze (IPGC) An addition-based puzzle using larger numbers. The children will need to be systematic.

Stars and circles (IPGC) This activity explores the beginnings of early algebra. It is better done as a group task to allow discussion of the answers.

❏ Try the values the other way around (○ = 15, ☆ = 10). Are any boxes still worth the same? Why? If you use ○ = 2 and ☆ = 3, how much is each box worth?

Triple totals (IPG) On this sheet, position is used to stress the value of tens and units. The children will need two of each of the number cards 1 to 9 (page 140).

❏ What is the smallest number the children can get? Use two copies of the sheet and play it as a game. As an alternative, let the children try multiplying the numbers. At a higher level, the probability of different results could be explored.

Matching minus (IPG) By subtraction and comparison the children should find that there are four cards for each total (6, 21, 37, 42, 47 and 87). The calculator is used to help them to check their working and to allow confidence to develop. The cards can be used to play the game of 'Pairs'. Have a calculator available to help the children to referee. Alternatively, play a card game where four cards are dealt to each player who may exchange one card at a time with the pack, taking turns. The winner is the first player with three cards with the same answer. Also play 'Snap' slowly.

Digit spinners (IPG) Copy the spinners on to card, cut them out and add cocktail sticks, or use plastic spinning arrows. Use these spinners for generating and playing with numbers.

❏ What proportion of the time do the children get answers which are more than 100? Help them to draw graphs to show their results. At a higher level, the probability of getting different results could be explored.

Points for circles (IPG) Through addition, this sheet explores the beginnings of algebra.

❏ Can the children design a box worth 9 points, 27 points or 8 points? Change the value of the circle to 36 points and encourage the children to rework the sheet. Use other values.

Lines of three (P) This game encourages mental arithmetic, addition practice and strategy. It is played like 'Noughts and crosses', except that more than one line of three is possible. To play, the children will need the 1 to 10 number cards (page 140) and a set of 12 counters each.

How long is a line? (IP) This sheet is about interpreting a real situation and matching it with a calculation.

❑ Using one of the spinners provided on page 56, ask the children to spin a digit and then make up a calculation which gives that digit as the answer. Can the children draw a picture which illustrates the calculation?

Line totals (IPG) Using a calculator allows several attempts so that the work is self-checking.

❑ Encourage the children to design their own lines and totals.

Tens and units words to add (IP) This sheet builds on 'Words to add' on page 44.

❑ Let the children work in pairs and use the tens and units number rollers (the nets are provided on page 131) to generate sets of five number words to add; one child doing the adding and the other checking the totals.

Memory trail (IPGC) This is an excellent way to encourage mental addition and subtraction; children often go off to try this on their parents. *Answers:* 10; 5; 7; 28; 4; 15.

❑ Can the children finish on 10 after ten uses of M+ or M-?

How long are the pencils? (IPG) This activity links measurement and addition. A similar activity could be carried out practically with pieces of string or ribbon.

❑ The children could go on to find the mean lengths of three pencils or four pencils and so on. How many different triangles can they make using the pencils? What is the perimeter of each?

Towards Level 4

Going visiting (IP) Practice in all four operations. *Answer:* hedgehog is going to visit bird.

❑ What is the largest total that the children can collect when visiting any animal without visiting any island twice?

Number cubes (IPG) On these dice the opposite faces add up to 10, 12, 8 and 14. The children will need to be systematic in order to check all the possibilities.

❑ Make two more cubes to move on to three-figure numbers or three two-figure numbers. How many even numbers can be found, or odd numbers, or multiples of 5, 7 and so on?

Calculatorpedes (P) This game uses the four rules. The children will need the three digit spinners provided on page 56.

❑ Alternatively, to move from one number to the next spin one digit and colour the segment if the number is divisible by the digit. Or, use three number cubes (the nets are provided on page 65) to play the original game.

Three together (P) This is a game which encourages lots of mental subtraction if you intend to win.

❑ Cut the calculation cards from the bottom of the page and use them to play 'Pairs', by matching the units digit.

Totally amazing (IPGC) Lots of addition practice is offered on this sheet. The children will need to be very systematic to find all 20 possible routes. *Answers:* lowest total 110 + 124 + 127 + 127 = 488; highest total = 173 + 170 + 169 + 166 = 678.

❑ Is it possible to design a route where half the totals are even and half are odd?

Pony jumps (P) This game explores addition and subtraction of larger numbers and encourages recording of operations. The children do not necessarily have to make each jump with one operation. They could try to create each number from 0, but a multiplication must be used. For example, 45 would be reached by jumping a log such as 4 × 11 + 1, or 9 × 5. Alternatively, they must use the square key or use division with the answer correct to the nearest whole number.

Mystery keystrokes (IPG) There are a number of ways to do each of these; for example, the second one could be 10 + + = 0 or 27 + + 10 = 0 or 993 + + 10 = 0.

❑ Play a game where one person sets up the keystrokes, and then each player asks for a number to be entered, until someone is ready to guess the keystrokes.

English sovereigns (IPGC) This activity uses lots of challenging subtraction. Talk about sensible and stupid answers. Is 'between' inclusive or exclusive? Point out sovereigns who ruled twice.

❑ Draw a diagram to show the lengths of the reigns of the sovereigns. Who reigned the longest? Who were the youngest sovereigns?

Product pairs (IPG) Although concentrating on multiplication practice, the sorting develops those cues which aid mental checking.

❑ Use the cards to play 'Pairs'.

Exploring multiplication (IPGC) Use the multiplication grid provided on page 143. This sheet offers another way of looking at multiples. At the lower levels it offers work on looking at a table and division, while at a higher level prediction, justification and generalisation should be encouraged as discoveries are made.

The soroban: 1 (IPGC) The abacus is a practical way to look at place value. By using the calculator to obtain the numbers the idea of 135 being 100 + 30 + 5 can be reinforced. *Answers:* the correct order is 5784, 3355, 7807, 5082, 6616.

❑ Use counters to put the same numbers on to the line abacus. Make a soroban. Use it to do some addition and subtraction. What numbers are made if any three beads are by the bar?

The soroban: 2 (IPGC) This activity provides practice on place value. The children can consider ranges of possible values and maximum and minimum numbers.

Rolling operations (IPG) A turn might be: the dice show 2 and 3 and the roller shows 'Double larger', $3 \times 2 = 6$ so $2 + 6$ gives 8. Then the dice may show 4 and 6 and the roller may show 'Find the difference' which gives 2, so the total so far is 10. If the dice then show 3 and 3 and the roller gives 'Back to 0' that means that that person's turn scores a total of 0, as all the previous scores are lost!

❑ Digit spinners (given on page 56) or number rollers (the nets are given on pages 131 and 132) or classroom-made spinners could be used to generate the numbers. As an alternative ending, score the mean of the five rounds with closest to 10 as the winner, or let the lowest score win.

Check those prices (IPG) The children will need a pack of 'Price label cards' (page 142).

❑ Can the children design and answer their own questions, testing them on others?

Amazing products (IPG) This activity can be used to encourage justification of answers in terms of factors and multiples. Different routes give a variety of different answers.

One for primes (PG) A game about multiples and factors.

❑ Use a digit spinner (from page 56 or classroom-made) instead of a dice.

Place value check (IP) This is a self-checking activity looking at numbers by place position.

Pentomino puzzle (IPG) This is really challenging! It could keep everyone going for weeks, or someone could be lucky and spot them all very quickly.

❑ Cut out the pentominoes. Which ones fold to make an open box? What do the boxes have in common?

Answer:

3	8	9	14	17	8	8	9	14	11
16	3	5	7	16	3			15	15
3	16	7	16	7	5	3		7	3
	13	15	11	11	16			10	4
	10	8	8	13	13	16	9	16	10
			16	8	17	3	6	8	11

Memory search (IPGC) A good activity for encouraging mental addition, since the working totals are hidden when using the memory.

❑ Discuss why it might be useful to use M+, rather than +, when adding a long column of figures. Let the children try using M-.

Using the +/- key (IPG) This activity helps children to explore the +/- key.

❑ Use the cards to play 'Pairs'.

Take a stride (IPGC) Work on this as a group activity on length. Finding a reasonable estimate of someone's stride length should raise lots of practical and numerical issues.

Lots of rectangles (IPG) Based on measuring and adding and/or multiplying a set of measurements for rectangles measured to the nearest mm. This activity and the following one assume prior knowledge of perimeter and area calculation.

Hexagons galore (IPG) Measure the sides to the nearest mm. A 4cm square drawn on to tracing paper may be useful. Or, you could try drawing the shapes on to square dotty paper.

There and back again (IPGC) This activity looks at 'doing' and 'undoing', as every number should finish unchanged.

❑ Cut up one of the flow charts and rearrange it in a different order so that the numbers still start and finish the same.

Squares of numbers (IPGC) You may need to reinforce the concept of squaring numbers first ($X \times X = X^2$).

❑ Ask the children to square the numbers from 1 to 12 and shade them on the multiplication grid (page 143). Let them try squaring consecutive even (or odd) numbers and finding the differences.

Product squares (IPG) This puzzle requires a lot of patience, like any jigsaw, with the calculator to offer speed, but the clues within the numbers may offer mental cues.

Answer – for example:

15 × 60 50 × 18 5 × 24 20 × 6	9 × 48 24 × 5 9 × 42 3 × 64	54 × 7 18 × 21 64 × 12 9 × 42
40 × 3 36 × 12 3 × 144 9 × 48	8 × 24 6 × 72 32 × 24 25 × 36	3 × 126 16 × 48 12 × 75 6 × 63
18 × 24 16 × 12 10 × 12 5 × 180	100 × 9 4 × 30 32 × 6 7 × 54	18 × 21 4 × 48 25 × 36 128 × 6

Towards Level 5

Decimal digit spins (IPG) A useful game for ordering decimal numbers.

❑ How many goes does each player have to have before they score 10 or more? Allow the use of operations. What results do the children get if they imagine the numbers on the number cards are 0.1, 0.2 and so on?

Hexagon hunt (IPG) To find a finishing number of 10, most pupils will use trial and improvement, which develops number awareness and ideas of the combined effects of different routes. By offering lots of different ending numbers, some children may begin to work backwards.

Percentage keys (IPGC) If possible, find a calculator which uses the key presses + 10 %, to make these percentage sheets much easier.
Answers: 220, 330, 82.5, 275, 27.5; 60, 230, 50.5, 606, 603.

Percentage four-in-a-row: 1 (P) This activity offers children a chance to get a feel for percentages before they are 'taught'.
It is intended to be played by trial-and-improvement, so that eventually the players begin to notice something about what happens when you add 10%.
❑ Let them try using 'Subtract 50%' or 'Add 100%'.

Percentage four-in-a-row: 2 (P) By using trial and improvement methods, this game helps the children to develop some feeling for 'Add 20%'.
❑ Use 'Add 50%', 'Subtract 40%', or 'Subtract 25%'. Handicap players of differing abilities by allowing two attempts at a number for the weaker player.

Percentage of (IPGC) If calculators with fraction buttons are available it is worth the children working with both types. The activity also considers equivalent fractions.
Answers: 20%, 10%, 75%, 46%, 80%, 20%, 20%, 1%, 8%, 25%.
❑ What fractions will give 20%?

Percentage three together (P) This game needs to be played a number of times. Using trial-and-improvement will help the children to develop better mental pictures for percentages. If the number chosen is 100, then the percentage will always be in the range.

Range attack (P) This is a useful game to develop ideas of approximate answers and their position on a number line.
❑ Try changing the range numbers.

Decimal number lines (IPG) A self-checking activity on reading decimals on number lines.
❑ The children can be encouraged to create their own number lines and totals.

A mean puzzle (IPG) You may need to revise finding means. The final stages of this activity require patience and a lot of addition – a good group activity.
Answer:

20	23	22	18	17
21	15	21	24	19
22	21	18	17	22
18	22	19	23	18
19	19	20	18	24

Heptagon angles (IPG) The internal angles of a heptagon should add up to 900°. The measuring of the angles is likely to be imprecise, offering an opportunity to discuss error.
❑ Let the children try measuring the angles of some other polygons.

A mean deal (P)
❑ Let the children try using only four cards and working out the means and ranges – is this a fairer game? Let them try dealing seven cards into two sets: one of four and one of three cards. Alternatively, let them use the 'Pocket money toy cards' (page 141) or 'Price label cards' (page 142).

Dog data (IPGC)
❑ The children could try answering the questions again, but using more than one of any dog. The children could design their own questions. How many Yorkshire Terriers do you need to balance a German Shepherd?
Answers: 56.1kg; Chihuahua, Jack Russell and Yorkshire Terrier; for example, St Bernard + German Shepherd + Yorkshire Terrier; for example, Cocker Spaniel + Jack Russell + Yorkshire Terrier + German Shepherd = St Bernard.

Spending for Oxfam (IPGC) This is a good activity for dealing with large numbers and getting a feel for things; guessing and testing is the best way of getting an idea. Refining guesses is a good topic for group discussion.
Answers: £3773584.90; £1400000; £1000000.
❑ Can the children express the pie chart in percentages/fractions/ decimals/angles?

A decimal hunt (IPGC) This activity contains a deceptive amount of work and requires ideas of place value.
❑ Use 'Is the answer 53?' (or other numbers) in the last box of the flow chart.

The Great Divider (PG) A game which focuses on the range for the answer when choosing which numbers to divide.
❑ Change the scoring system (the current one favours the smaller number divided by larger).

Hexagon multiplication (P) A good game, using trial-and-improvement methods, to develop mental strategies.
❑ Play 'Is divisible by': state a number on the board and divide by a number in the box. If the result is a whole number, claim the hexagon.

Honeycomb division (P) Another game using trial-and-improvement methods to develop mental strategies.

❑ Alternatively, the children could play 'Gozinter': choose a number on the board and divide it into a number in Box 1, if the result is a whole number claim the hexagon.

Square capture (P) Using trial-and-improvement methods develops mental strategies. This style of game does not have to be played to the 'end', but could have time limits.

❑ Alternatively, let the children play 'Is divisible by': state a number on a bar, divide by a number in the box, if the result is a whole number claim the bar.

Heartbeats (IPGC) This activity explores using big numbers and is ideal for a group to work on. Finding a sensible way of measuring and calculating their own heartbeats will provide some useful scientific discussion and decision-making, for example, 'How long is a month?'

Towards Level 6

Fractions and decimals (IPGC) This is very much easier than the level suggests. If calculators with fraction buttons are available encourage the children to work with both types. The activity offers a chance to consider equivalent fractions, as well as changing fractions to decimals.

❑ Extend to percentages. Draw number lines to show the fraction, decimal and percentage equivalents. What fractions give decimals bigger than 0.2, but smaller than 0.25?

Range roulette (PG) Another game which looks at range for the results of multiplication. The children will need a plastic spinning arrow available from Tarquin or to make up the board with the pointer provided. Stick the roulette board and the pointer on to the card and cut them out. Make a hole in the pointer with a hole punch. Push the paper fastener loosely through the hole in the pointer and through the centre of the board. Put a piece of sticky tape on the underside of the board across the fastener to stop it moving and to protect the children's fingers. It is recommended that the board is enlarged to A3.

❑ Use division instead.

Keep pressing (IPGC) The children will need to use the multiplication grid provided on page 143. Through this flow chart the children can use the √ key to discover some 'strange' numbers. The children may encounter the 'infinite loop' – when do they stop...?

Rush to estimate (PG) The children will need the 'Price label cards' (page 142). This game develops mental addition and estimation.

❑ Try these variations: change the time limits, use the 'Pocket money toy cards' (page 141), use more cards, use the number cards (page 140) and multiplication to the nearest 10.

Breathing (IPGC) This is best tackled as a group activity. Designing a reasonable method of estimating their own breathing rates should raise lots of practical and numerical issues.

Answers: the answers will depend on the assumptions made and ideas of 'an average'. In an hour, on average, a dolphin breathes 180 times and a sperm whale 144 times.

Communications (IPGC) This investigation is probably better organised as a group activity so that discussion can be encouraged. There are many ways to approach this investigation, based on the total or % urban population. Discuss whether the urban population are more likely to have TVs and so on.

The actual values cannot possibly be read from the diagram, so estimation must be considered. The true values (per 1000 people) are taken from *Third World Guide 93–94* (1992, Instituto del Tercer Mundo):

	Newspapers	TVs	Radios
Australia	252	484	1262
Brazil	48	204	373
India	28	27	78
Japan	566	610	895
UK	394	434	1145
USA	259	814	2122

Across the levels

Many of the sheets throughout this book can be used with children working at levels other than that specified. However, the sheets in this section demonstrate how particular activities can be differentiated for a variety of abilities.

Lots of patterns (IPGC) Very young pupils can be encouraged to predict while they are playing with patterns and digits. As a group/class activity, the results can be shared and discussed. At higher levels, the children should be encouraged to predict more formally, for example, what the 10th, 25th or 100th numbers will be. For patterns such as 123123..., several calculators can be used and the problem of which calculators have the same display considered, leading to ideas of common factors and multiples.

Arithmagon (IPG) The children will need the 1 to 6 number cards (provided on page 140) for this activity. By using number cards, so that the numbers can be moved easily, this activity is suitable for the youngest child. Lots of addition practice occurs even if they do not reach a solution. As the children revisit the problem you will see strategies developing. At higher levels, they can be encouraged to find more than one solution. Let them use other sets of numbers, for example 3, 4, 5, 6, 7, 8, 9 or consecutive even numbers, and find general solutions.

Answer – for example:

1

6 5

2 4 3

Humpty numbers (IPGC) The addition of numbers and the style of this activity is possible for children working towards Level 2. There are very many solutions so at higher levels, number patterns, general solutions and justification become important to the task.

❑ Can the children design some walls where Humpty is sitting on the number 50?

Hopscotch (IPGC) The playing board offers possibilities for children to make up calculations at any level in order to move along. Level 1 children can count to the numbers. At higher levels, they can use the board from left to right for addition and right to left for subtraction. Check that the totals of all the calculations are 35 or 36.

❑ Variations might include: changing the numbers, one player moving on odd numbers and the other on even, using five additions and five subtractions, using all multiplication or division only to get each number from scratch, or multiplying to get from one number to the next, ignoring any decimal places.

Constant counting (IPGC) This facility is accessible for all levels, and is one of the most useful attributes of the calculator. Level 1 children can look at pattern, recording digits and so on, but the material would be better presented to them orally. For older children the activity can be focused on to multiples. Let them use the number grids (pages 137–139) and shade in the multiples as they appear on the display – what different patterns do they make? This technique can be used to sort for prime numbers by shading on a hundred square all the multiples of 2 except 2, multiples of 3 except 3 and so on. Let them use the multiplication grid (page 143). As the pattern emerges (that is, 4, 8, 12...) connect the third multiple with 3 × 4 and so on. Go on to ask the children to generate the multiples of 7, writing down everything they can about the pattern in the units digit.

Counting backwards (IPGC) This work can be done with young children orally. Negative numbers will appear at an early stage, which young children appear to accept readily as 'the other way' on the number line.

❑ Work on multiples backwards. Let the children make patterns on the number grids (pages 137–139) by colouring differently the results of 50 – – 3 = =..., 49 – – 3 = =..., 48 – – 3 = = ... What starting point will allow them to have 12 and 2 in their set of numbers? What about 7 and –7?

Five, four, three, two, one (IPGC) From Level 1, the children can work on sums such as 1 + 3 + 4 + 5 + 2 =, or 2 + 4 + 3 + 5 + 1 = ... working towards commutativity (a + b = b + a), and variations such as 123 + 45 will soon appear. At higher levels, the children can work on ideas of highest/lowest results, divisibility by 3 and so on.

Mystery boxes (IPGC) Present Level 1 children with one task to work on in a group. Recording wrong results can be as much fun (and as valuable) as recording correct ones. At higher levels, a wider variety of possibilities will be explored. There are lots of opportunities for trial and improvement and guess and test.

Doubling (IPGC) Doubling, or duplation, used to be considered to be a separate operation from the four rules. It is very important in developing mental skills. Visit this task many times. For the game, the children will need copies of the 6 number grid, provided on page 138.

❑ Go on to consider 'double, double' (×4) and 'double, double, double' (×8).

Halving (IPGC) As with doubling, halving should begin very early. Halving, or mediation, can be practised across many levels. 'Which numbers halved give whole numbers?' can be used as an early test for even numbers.

❑ Give the children other finishing numbers which they have to reach with five halving operations. Extend halving to quartering and eighths, and multiples of four and eight. What is the 'half of' table? (1 × ½ = ½, 2 × ½ = 1... or, ½ of 2 is 1, ½ of 4 is 2... .)

Multiplying by 10 (IPGC) Multiplying by 10 should be introduced and reinforced on many occasions. Using a calculator means that rules need not be given out and practised, rather the children are able to play with numbers, including decimals, and develop operations and rules, using place value language.

Decimal discoverer (IPGC) Dividing by 10 can be used at many levels and connected to place value from a very early stage.

Steps to 100 (IPGC) For Level 1 children, this task is one of looking at digits and recognising whether they have passed the target, reinforcing 'more than/less than'. At higher levels, the children can work on factors. The number of steps required to reach 100 helps with products. Decimal addition can also be explored.

❑ Change the target number to 36 or 144 or 350. Alternatively, give the children the number of steps and ask them what target numbers they can find. Also try telling them that in reaching the target number they must go through and show 35 and 77, or 36 and 90 and so on.

What answers? (IPGC) This activity is for Level 2 onwards. There are lots of opportunities for justifying results and generalising ideas. Negative numbers are very likely to appear.

Line abacus numbers (IPGC) The children will need a copy of the line abacus provided on page 144 to use this sheet. For Level 3 and above, this activity will involve lots of trial and improvement. At higher levels, strategies for solutions should appear.
Answers: 2338; 3333; 1834; 1942.
❑ If you add a number that uses three counters to a number that uses three counters, can you have an answer that uses three counters?
Number word rollers: 1 (IPG) A high level of skill is needed to make these decagon prisms, but the rollers could be used at all levels to generate numbers. Level 1 children can roll the units roller and fill their calculator screens with the number, or roll it twice and make a repeating pattern. Level 2 children can work on sums and differences of a tens roller and a units roller.
Number word rollers: 2 (IPG) From Level 2 onwards, thousands and hundreds can be introduced for further place value work.
❑ Four-figure numbers can be rolled using all four rollers, and put on the line abacus (page 144) and the calculator. Ask the children to design games where the rollers are the element of chance. Or, ask them to roll a hundreds roller and a units roller; by what would they multiply the number on the units roller to get the number on the hundreds roller?
Exploring the multiplication grid (IPGC) This activity practises multiplication and using the tables grid (page 143). It also ensures that they can use a multiplication grid as well as a calculator. It is important to connect all the ways in which children work on division and multiplication.
The 4 × 4 magic square (IPGC) This work can either be trial and improvement (offering lots of opportunities for Level 3 children to work on addition) or it can be more strategic using number patterns. Higher level children should be encouraged to offer written justification for their results.
Duplation (IPGC) This is another way of using doubling. At higher levels the children should be encouraged to work on the ideas mentally, as well as with a calculator.

Resources

These sheets are used with others in the book, but you will find they have many more uses than are described here.
Digital paper Used for recording any calculator displays. What numbers can be made by colouring in five bars? Or 25? Or 17? If the first two numbers in a pattern use nine bars, can the children show the patterns?
3 and 4, 6, 10 number grids These different width grids are used in this book for recording multiples, but they have lots of other uses. The 2cm grid size allows plastic cubes to be used on the squares. Design 2, 5, 7, 8, 9, 11, 12 or 13 grids. They can be used to practise addition, subtraction, multiples and number patterns, or as game boards to play calculation games. If the children add a number from one of the first columns to the one below it, where does the answer appear? What about if they add up the whole first column, and the last column, what is the difference between the two totals? Ask them to find the difference between a number and one two rows below. On the 3 grid, choose a row and multiply the outside two numbers together and square the middle one. Compare the two answers. Do this for each row. Does this happen for any row of three on the other grids? On the 4 grid, choose any row and multiply the outside two numbers together and multiply the inside two numbers together. Compare the two answers. The 6 grid is especially good in the search for primes because of where the primes (except for 2 and 3) appear. Explore the differences between one number and another number one across two down, or two below and so on. Explore a 2 × 2 square within the grid by adding diagonal numbers or a 3 × 3 square within the grid by adding opposite numbers.
0 to 17 number cards Can the children divide the cards into two piles, each with the same total? This can be done using two to 18 cards. The number of cards in each pile does not have to be the same. Let the children go on to divide the cards similarly into three, four or five piles. Play 'Pairs' where the match is the difference between the two numbers is 9.
Pocket money toy cards Ask the children to divide the cards into two piles where the cost of one pile is about twice as much as the other. If a child buys ten toys, how much will they spend?
Price label cards Ask the children to divide the cards into two piles where the total for one pile is about £3 more than the other.
Multiplication grid Use this grid for division, factors, multiplication and multiples and looking at last digits. Explore a 2 × 2 square within the grid and then 3 × 3 square within the grid by multiplying the diagonally opposite numbers.
The line abacus Use this sheet with cubes or counters for place value calculations, addition, subtraction and doubling. Show the children how to play 'Place invaders', a game for 2 players. Tell one player to set up a number on a calculator and the abacus. The other must try to 'knock down' digits (make them 0) by subtracting carefully; for example, 4567 – 500 to remove the 5. How many counters does the player need to remove to show this on the abacus?

Name ____________________

Fill your display

You will need: some digital paper, a pencil and a calculator.

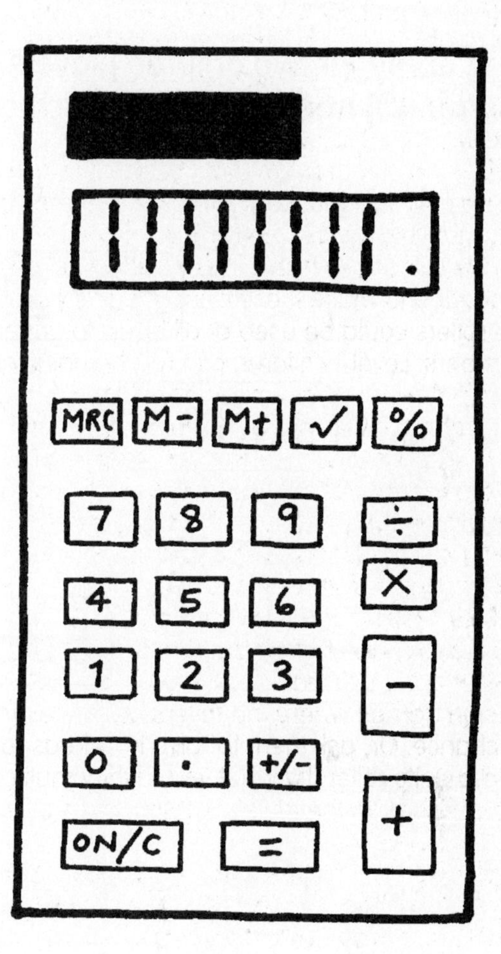

✤ Fill your display with 1s, so that your calculator looks like the picture shown here. Copy your pattern on to the digital paper.

✤ Fill your display with 2s. Copy your pattern on to the digital paper.

✤ Fill your display with 7s. Copy your pattern on to the digital paper.

✤ Fill your display with 8s. Copy your pattern on to the digital paper.

✤ Ask a friend to fill a calculator display with a number.
Copy this pattern.

✤ Can you fill your display with 0s?

✤ Design a pattern of numbers on the digital paper and then enter it on to the calculator display.

Name ______________________

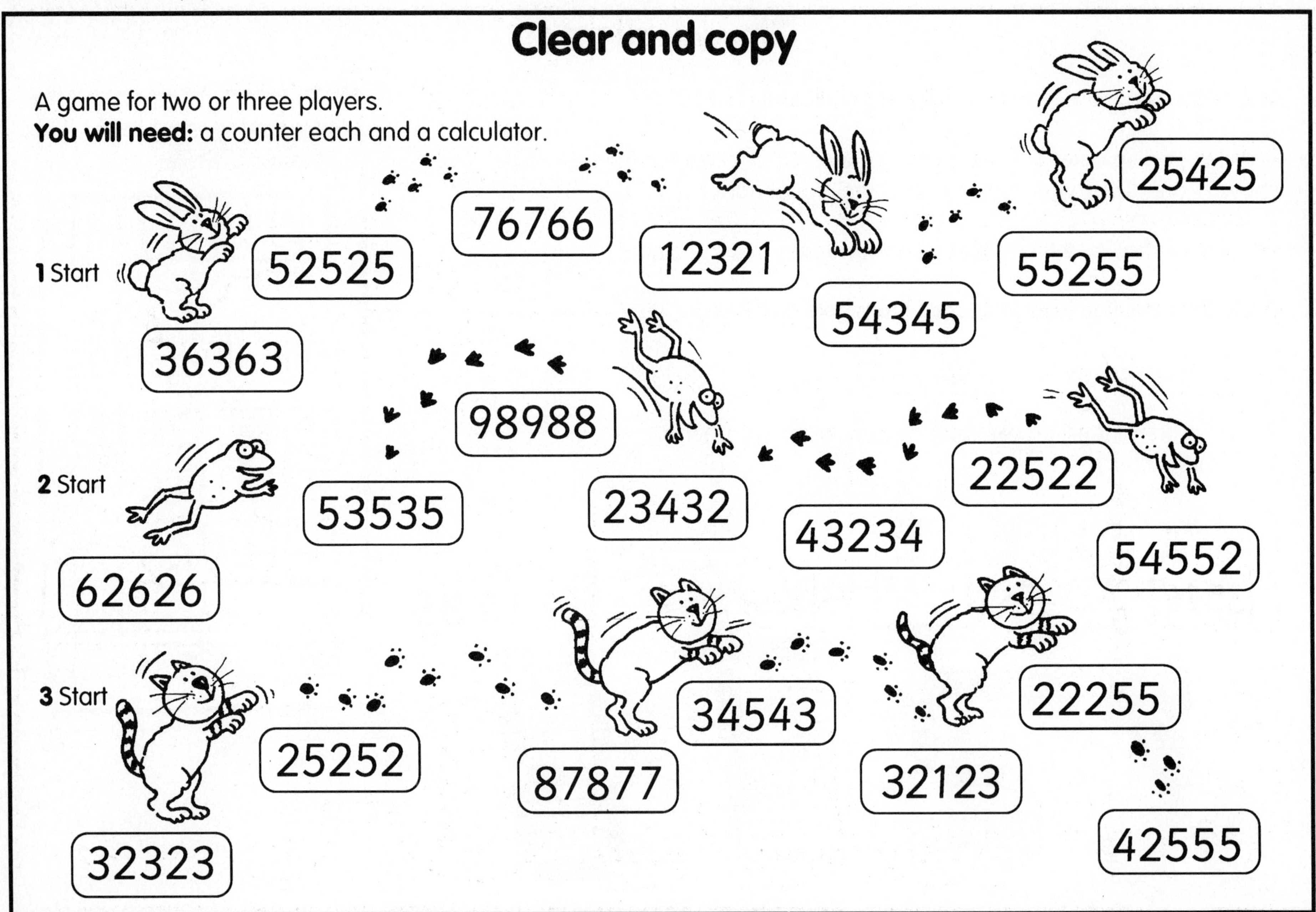

Clear and copy
A game for two or three players.
You will need: a counter each and a calculator.
1 Start
52525
36363
76766
12321
54345
55255
25425
2 Start
62626
53535
98988
23432
43234
22522
54552
3 Start
32323
25252
87877
34543
32123
22255
42555

Name ____________________

Train spotting

✤ Choose a number on a part of this picture.

✤ Enter the number carefully on to your calculator display.

✤ Check the display. If the number is correct, you can colour that part of the picture.

✤ Do this until you have coloured the whole picture.

Name ____________________

Counting cubes

You will need: some digital paper, plain paper, a pencil and a calculator.

✤ Find some cubes.

✤ Draw a picture of the cubes. How many are there? Fill the screen of your calculator with that number.

✤ Copy your display on to the digital paper.

For example:

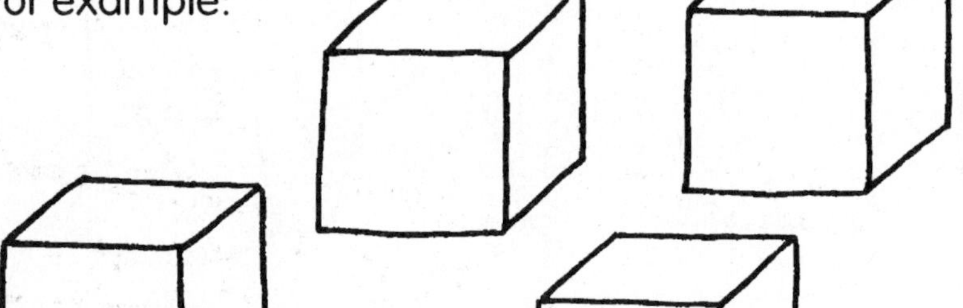

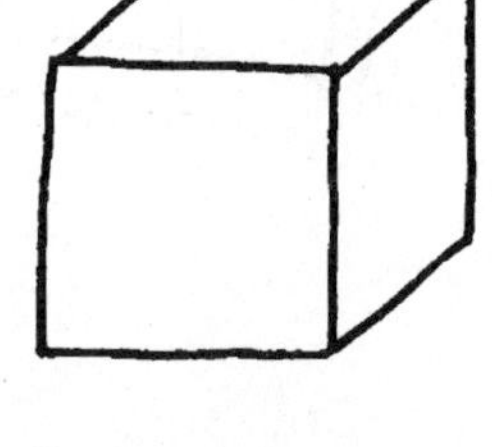

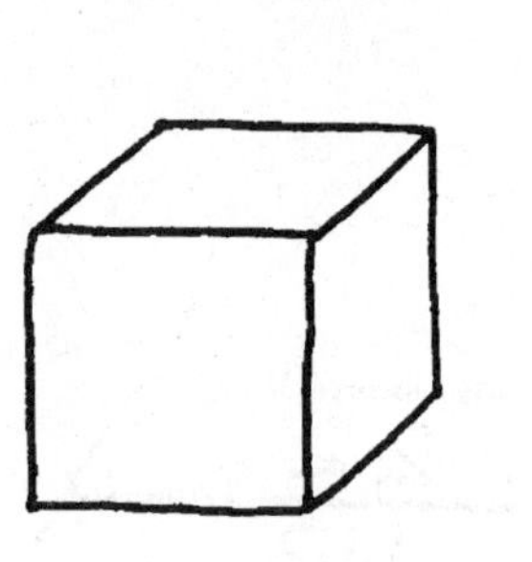

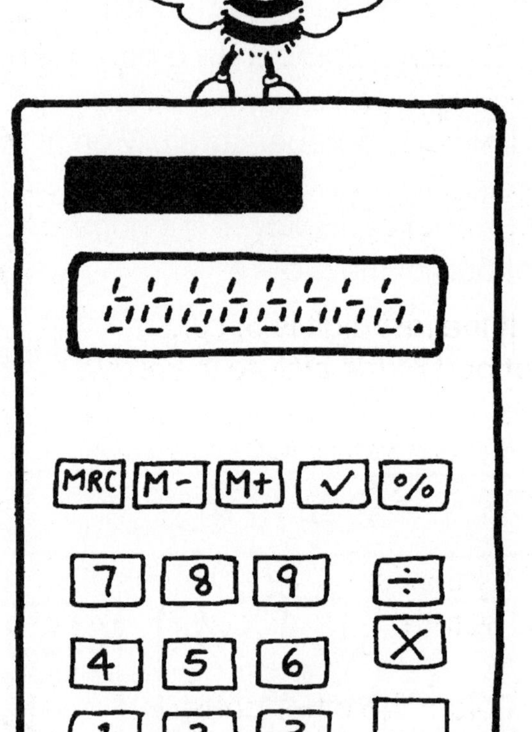

Name ______________________

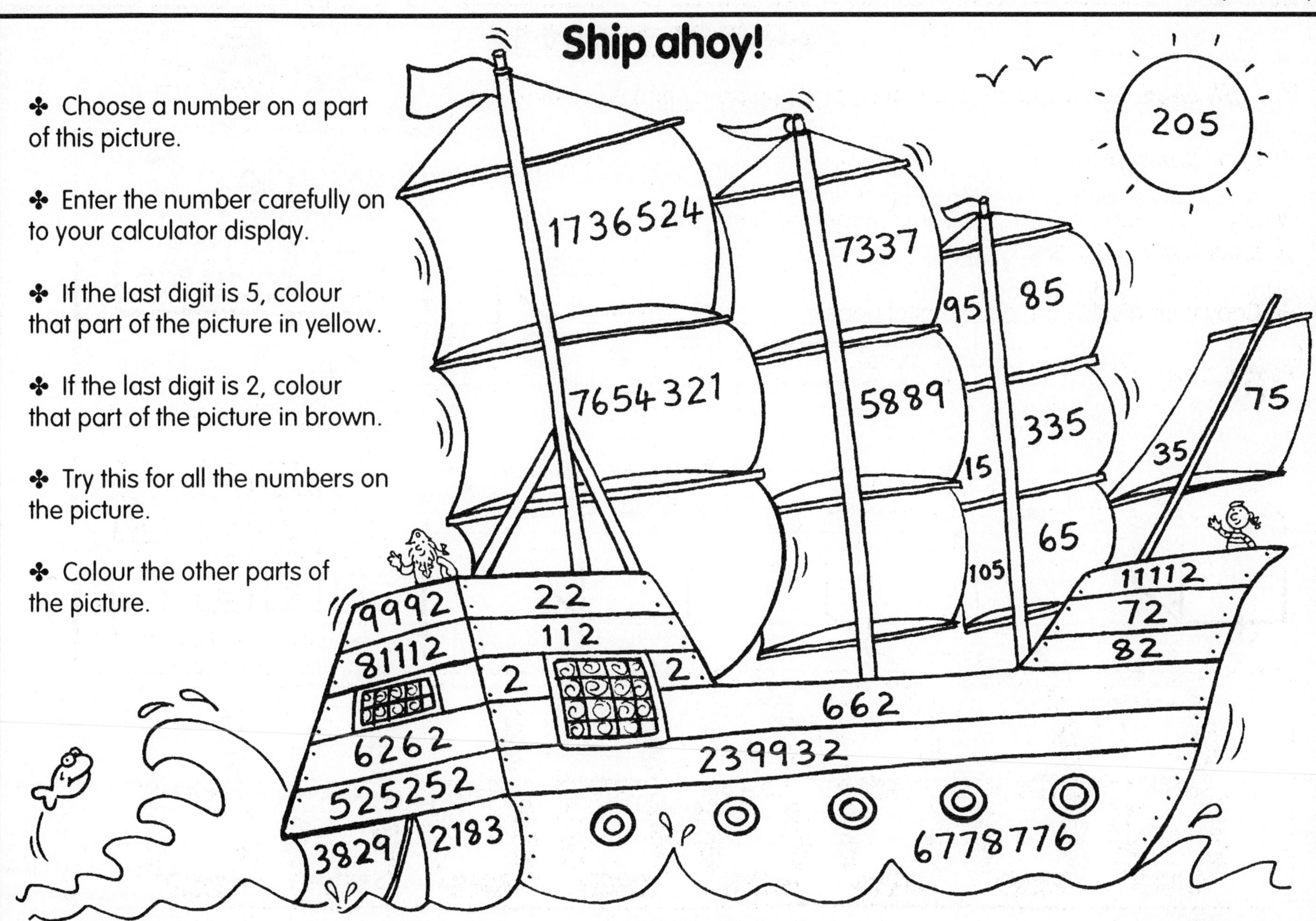
Ship ahoy!
✤ Choose a number on a part of this picture.
✤ Enter the number carefully on to your calculator display.
✤ If the last digit is 5, colour that part of the picture in yellow.
✤ If the last digit is 2, colour that part of the picture in brown.
✤ Try this for all the numbers on the picture.
✤ Colour the other parts of the picture.
205
1736524
7337
95
85
7654321
5889
335
75
35
15
65
105
11112
72
82
9992
22
112
81112
2
2
662
6262
239932
525252
3829
2183
6778776

Name ____________________

Count and display

You will need: some digital paper, a pencil and a calculator.

✣ What number is hidden on my calculator? Count the objects to find out. Each box gives you the clue to one digit.

✣ Put the numbers on to your calculator display and copy the whole display on to the digital paper.

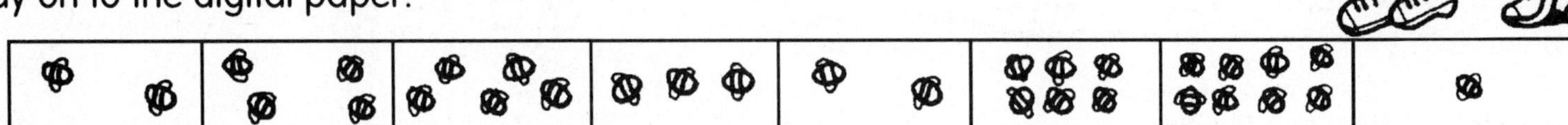

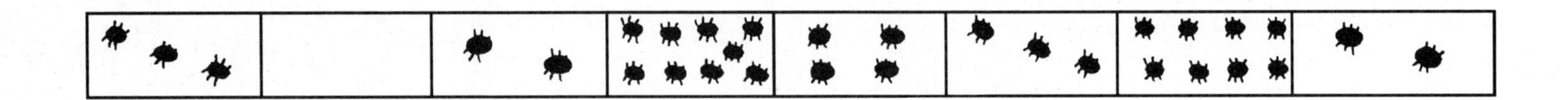

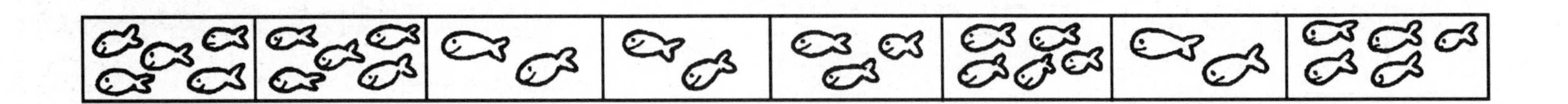

Name ____________________

Reversing Rita

You will need: some digital paper, a pencil and two calculators.

Reversing Rita always likes to reverse the digits on her calculator display. So if she is asked to show **25467814**, her calculator shows:

41876452

✤ Show what Reversing Rita's calculator display looks like by putting these numbers on your display in Rita's way:

12345678	34434434
98765432	12344321
93693693	24242424
82567122	35422453

✤ Copy each one on to digital paper.

✤ Use two calculators. Design your own display and show Rita's. Will the displays ever look the same?

Name ____________________

Symmetrical shields

You will need: some coloured pencils and a calculator.

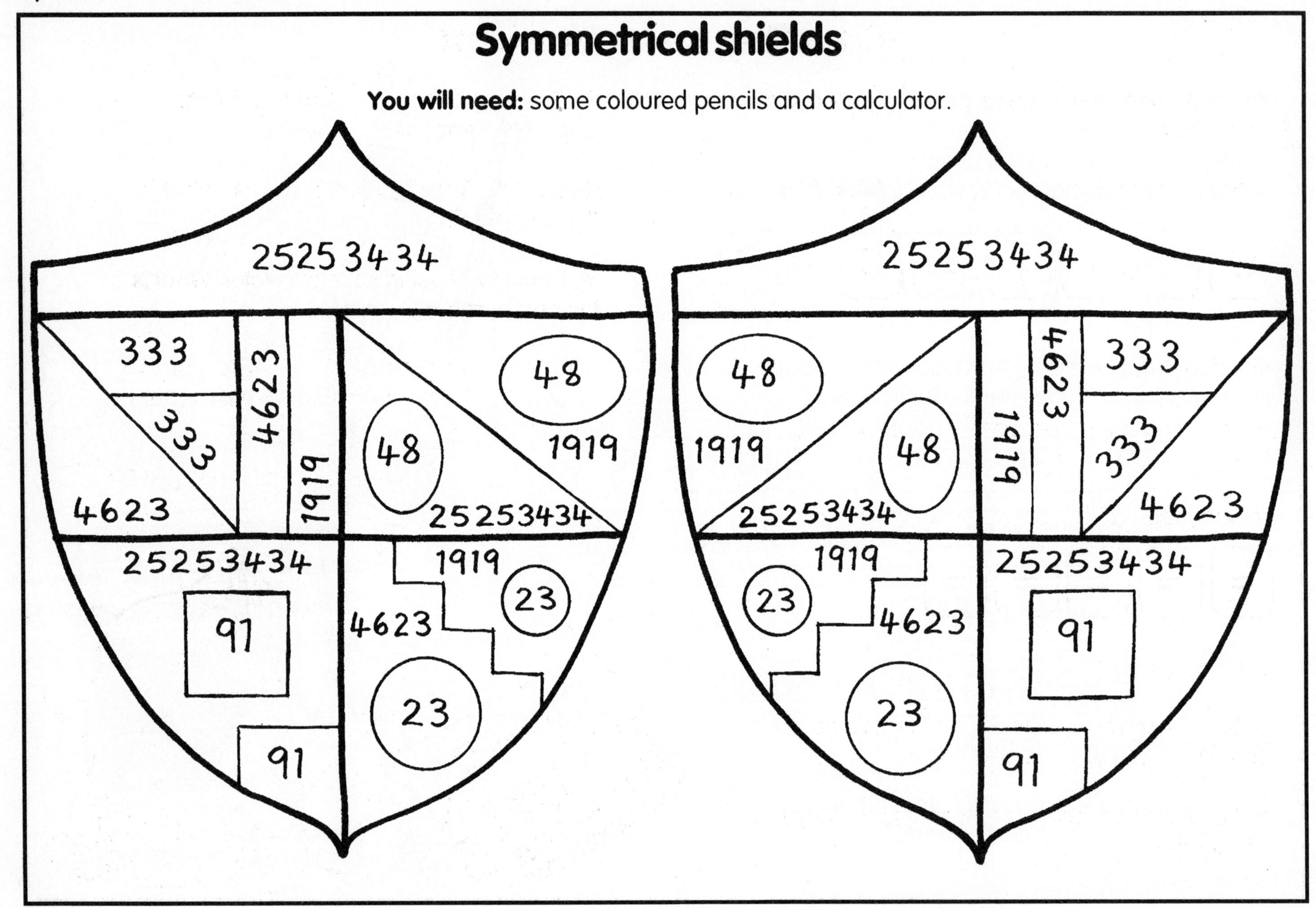

Name ______________

Counting on a calculator

You will need: some digital paper, a pencil and a calculator.

✤ Press these buttons on your calculator:

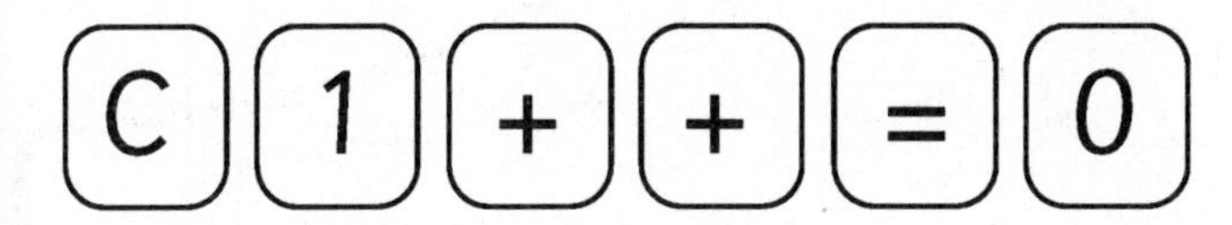

✤ Keep pressing the = button. What happens?

✤ Pick a number, then use this method to count up to that number.

For example, count up to 7 by pressing:

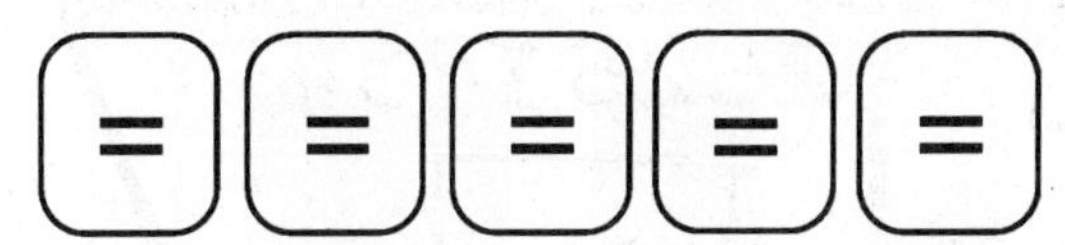

until you get to 7.

✤ Now clear your calculator and reset it as above. Count to 11. Copy the number.

✤ Reset your calculator and count to 23. Copy this number.

✤ Reset your calculator and count to 46. Copy this number.

✤ Count to 9 using your calculator. What is the next number?

✤ Count to 19 using your calculator. What is the next number?

✤ Count to 29, 39, 49, 59, 69, 79, 89 and 99 in turn. What is the next number after each of these?

How many?

✤ Set up your calculator to count in 1s by pressing these buttons:

C 1 + + = 0

✤ Touch each star in the first box and at the same time press = . Write down the number you stop at.

✤ Do the same for these circles.

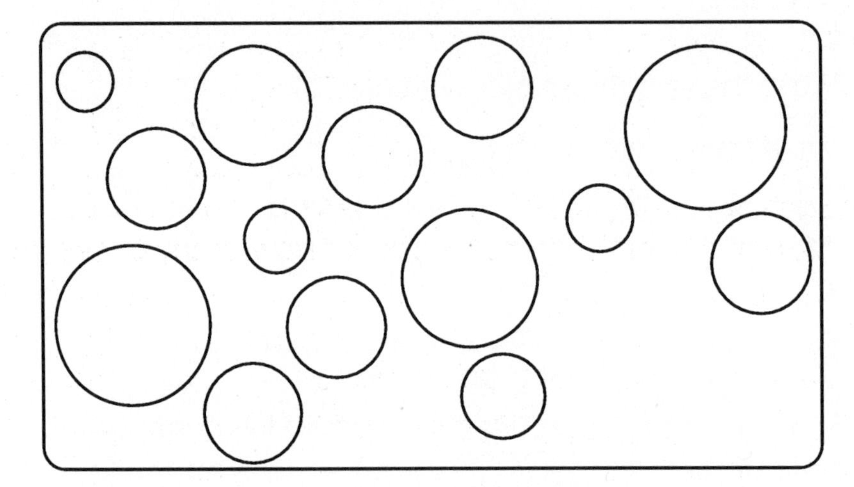

✤ Do the same for these squares.

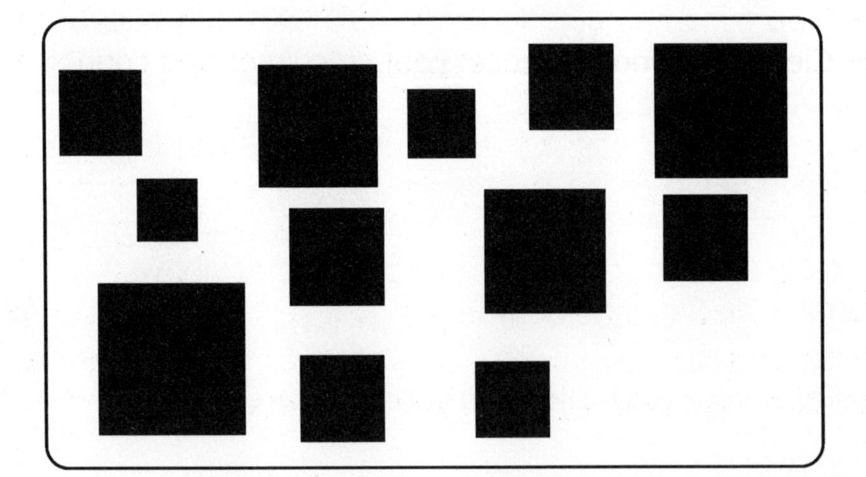

Name ____________________

Cubes and grids

You will need: a number grid, some cubes and a calculator.

- Set up your calculator to count in 1s by pressing these buttons:

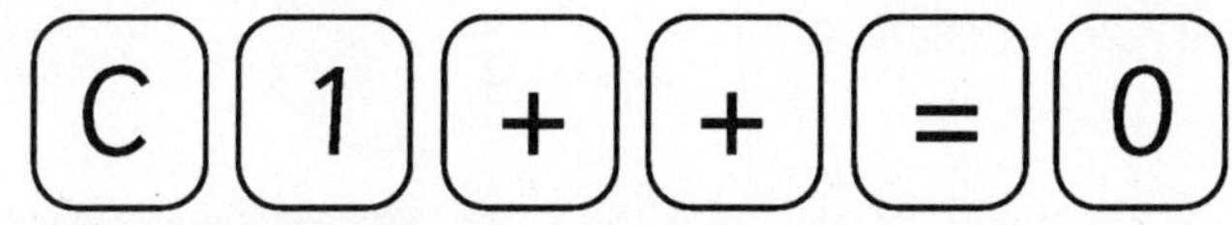

C 1 + + = 0

- Each time you press = put **one** cube on the correct number on the grid.
- Stop at any number and work out how many cubes are on the grid.
- Clear your grid and reset your calculator and count to a different number of cubes.

- Set up your calculator to count in 2s by pressing these buttons:

C 2 + + = 0

- Each time you press = put **two** cubes on the correct number on the grid.
- Stop at some point and work out how many cubes are on the grid.
- Clear your grid and reset your calculator and count to a different number of cubes.

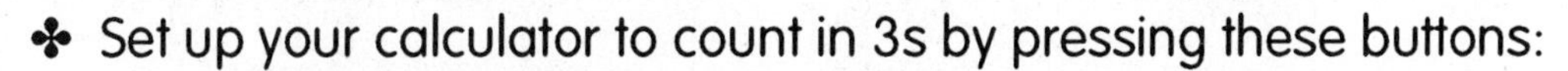

- Set up your calculator to count in 3s by pressing these buttons:

C 3 + + = 0

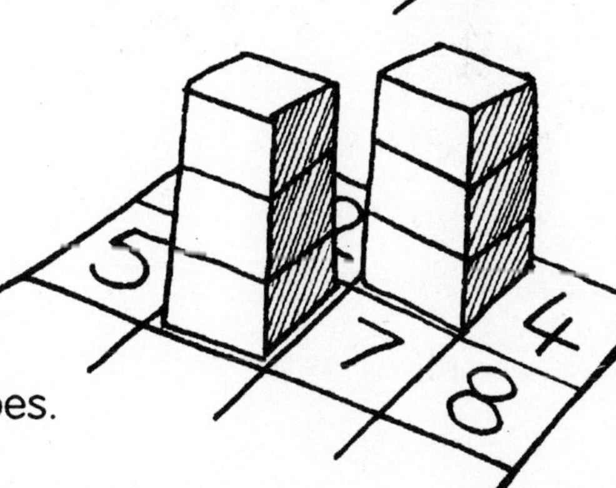

- Each time you press = put **three** cubes on the correct number on the grid.
- Stop at some point and work out how many cubes are on the grid.
- Clear your grid and reset your calculator and count to a different number of cubes.

Name ____________________

Cubes to add

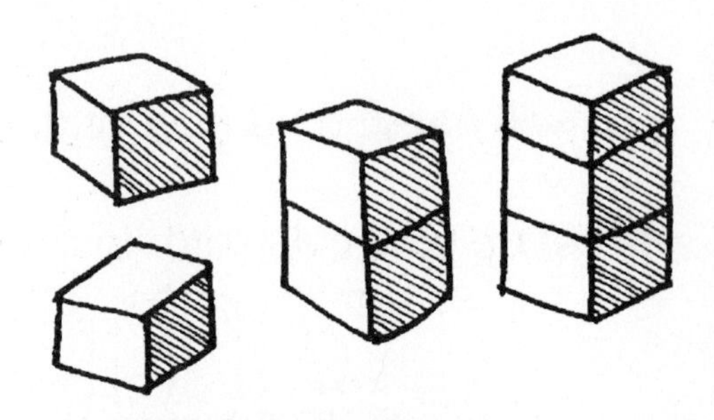

You will need: some cubes, the 1 to 9 number cards and a calculator.

✤ Deal two cards and place them on the spaces below. Put the correct number of cubes into each circle. Count the cubes. Do the addition on the calculator.

✤ Do this lots of times.

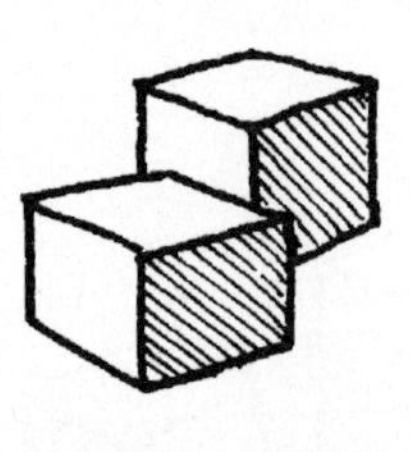

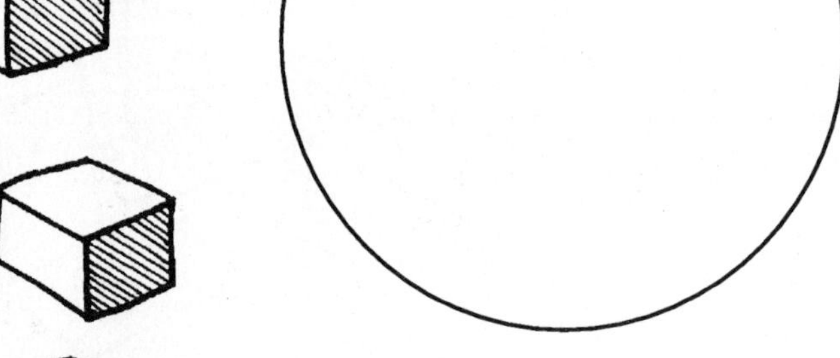

Cubes

Cubes

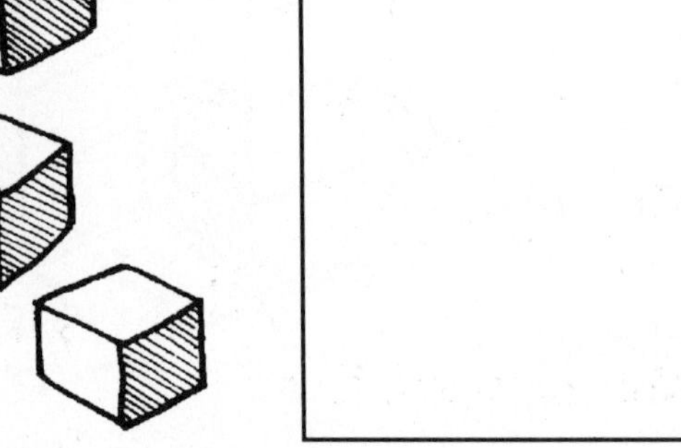

Number card

+

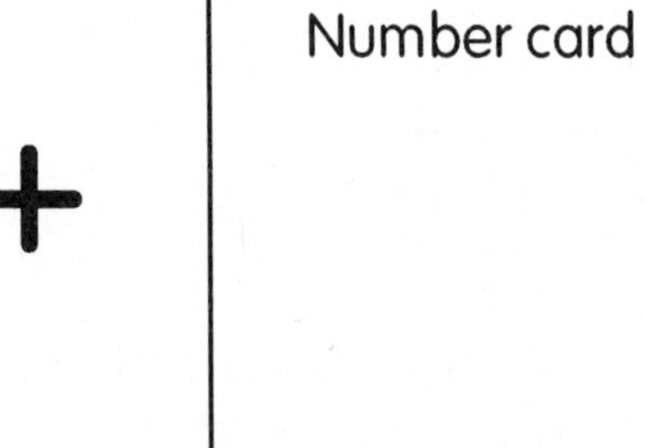

Number card

=

Name ____________________

Constant dots

✣ Set up your calculator to count in 1s by pressing these buttons: [C] [1] [+] [+] [=] [0]

✣ Each time you press [=], find the number below and join the dots one at a time in the correct order.

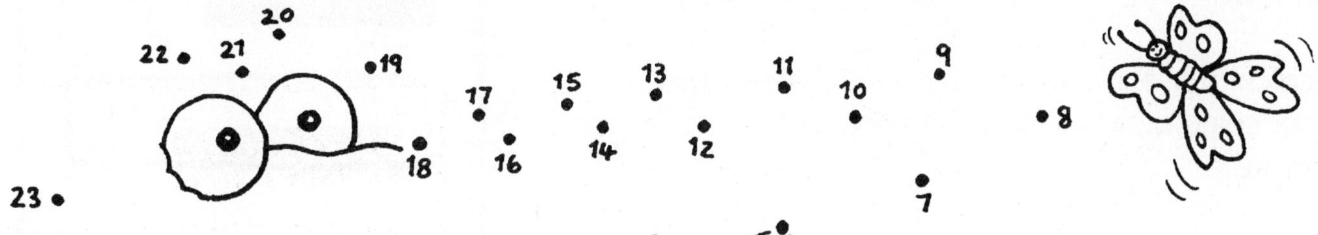

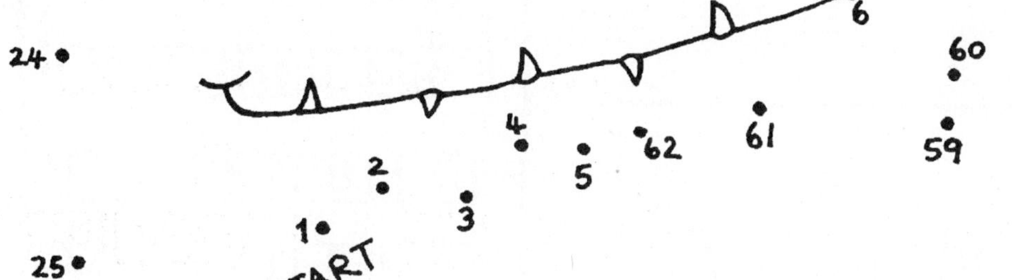

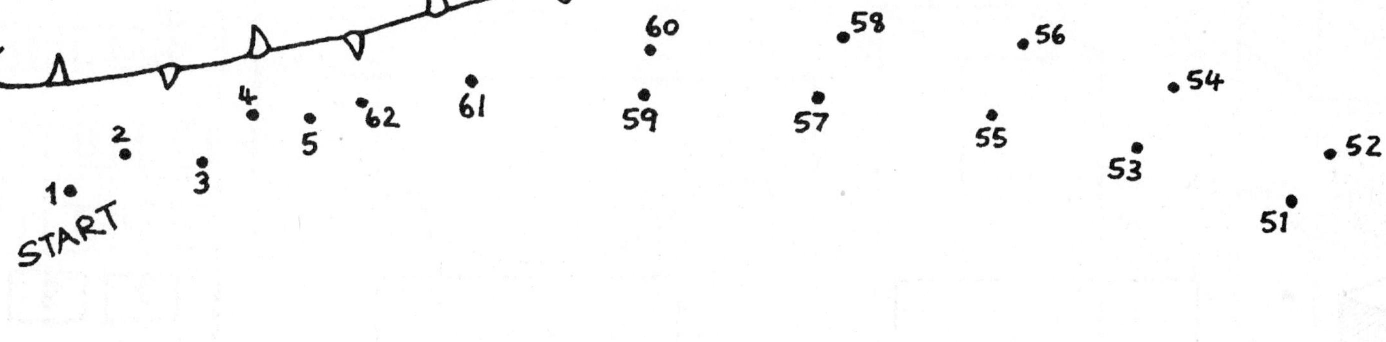

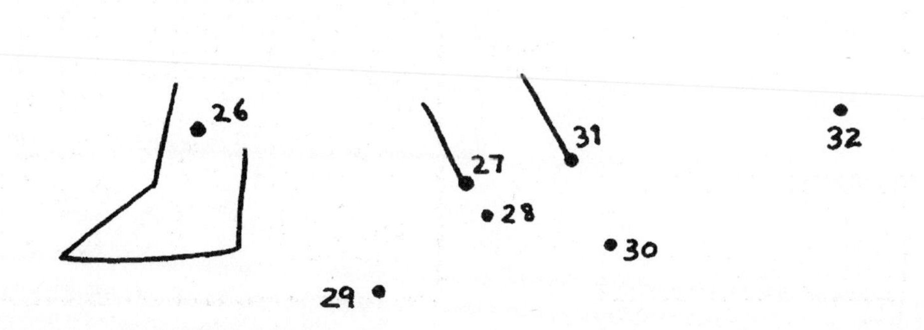

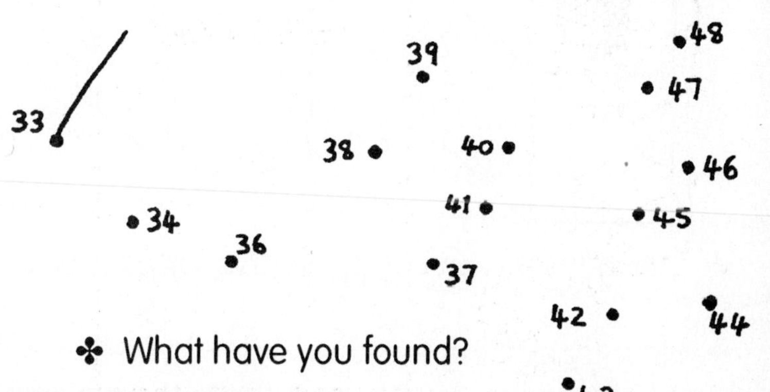

✣ What have you found?

Name ____________________

Number towers

You will need: seven cubes, a pencil, paper and a calculator.

✤ Build the cubes into two towers. Draw a picture of the two towers. How many cubes are there in each tower?

✤ What calculation on your calculator can you use to connect these two numbers to get the 7? Use your calculator to help you to find out.

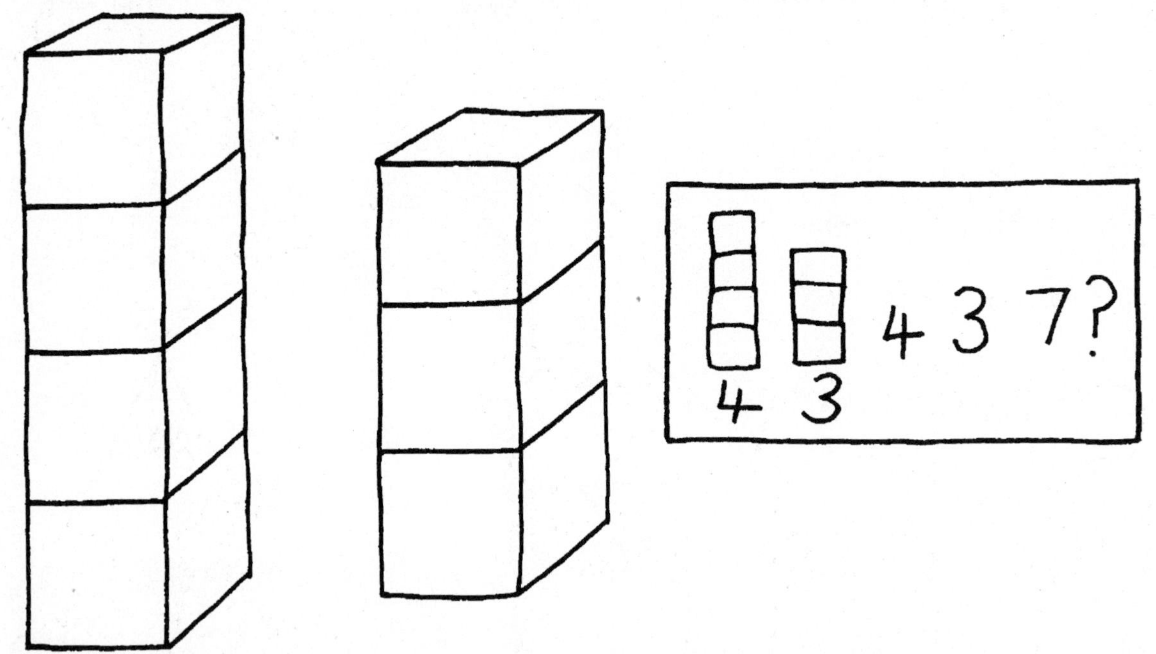

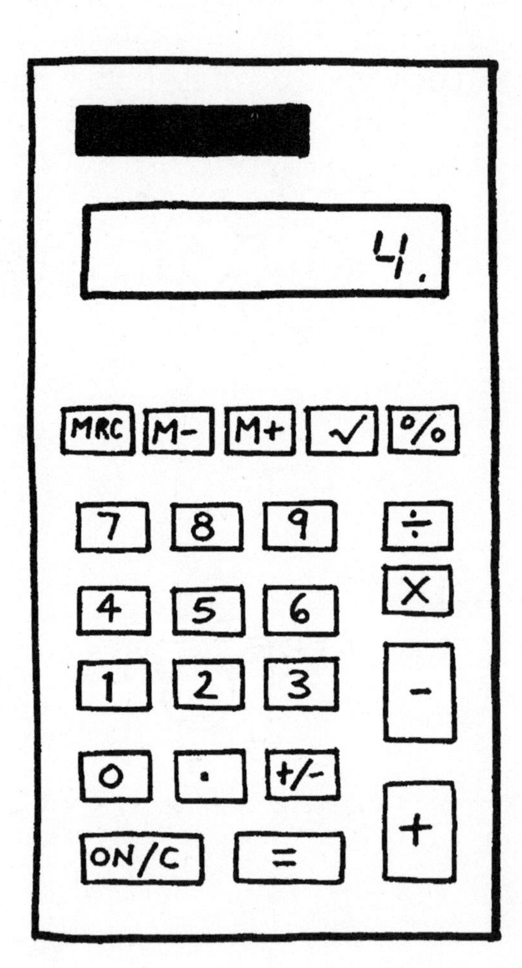

✤ Using the seven cubes, try this for as many pairs of towers as you can.

✤ Now try making three towers. How many cubes are there in each tower? How can you connect these three numbers and the 7?

Name ____________

Totem totals

✤ Put some numbers in the post of the totem pole that will add up to the number in the circle on the top. Use your calculator to help you. The first one has been done for you.

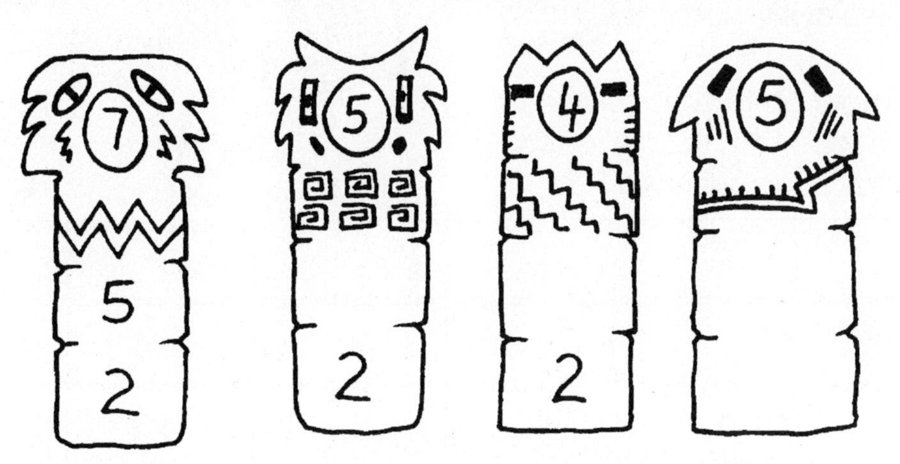

✤ Now make up some whole totem pole sums for yourself.

Name ______________

Number hunt

You will need: some digital paper, a pencil and a calculator.

What numbers are hidden in these calculator displays?

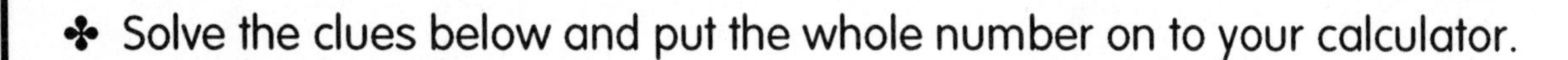

✤ Solve the clues below and put the whole number on to your calculator.

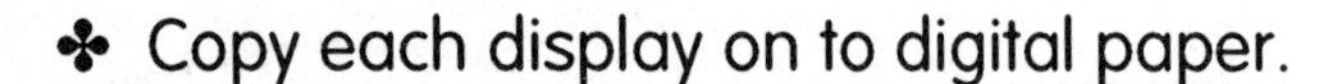

✤ Copy each display on to digital paper.

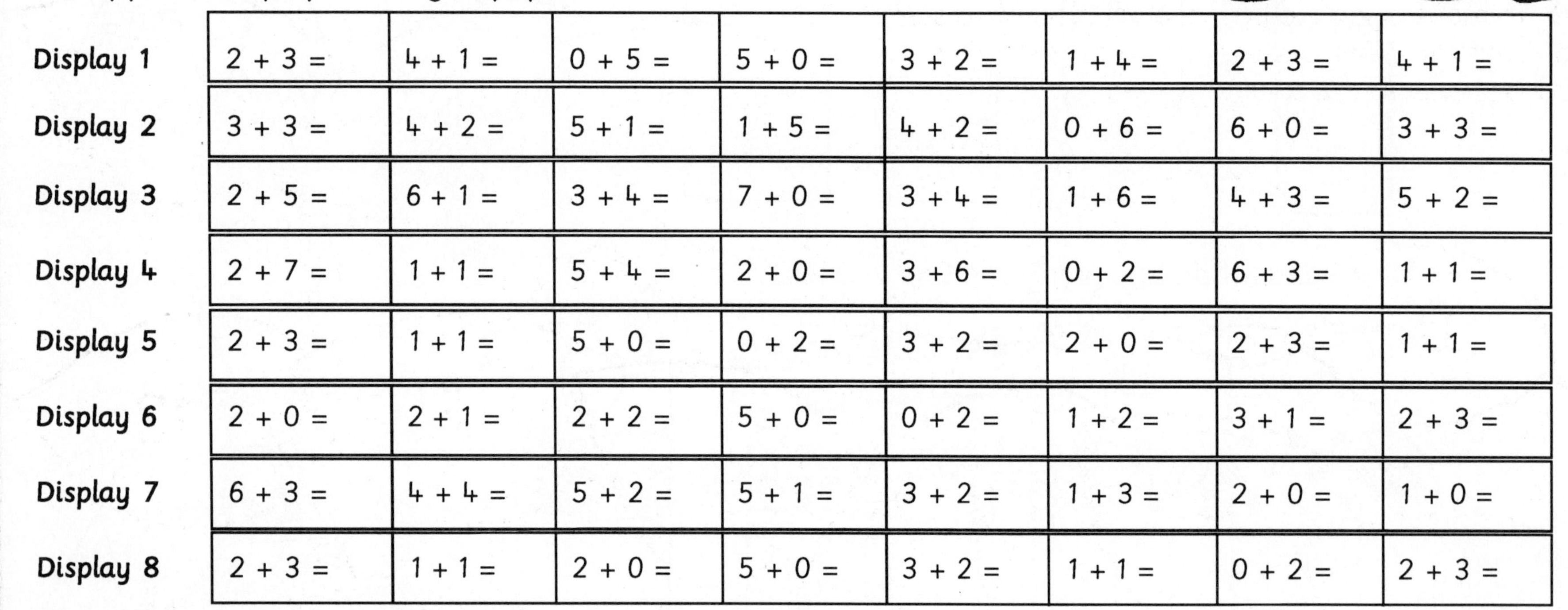

Display 1	2 + 3 =	4 + 1 =	0 + 5 =	5 + 0 =	3 + 2 =	1 + 4 =	2 + 3 =	4 + 1 =
Display 2	3 + 3 =	4 + 2 =	5 + 1 =	1 + 5 =	4 + 2 =	0 + 6 =	6 + 0 =	3 + 3 =
Display 3	2 + 5 =	6 + 1 =	3 + 4 =	7 + 0 =	3 + 4 =	1 + 6 =	4 + 3 =	5 + 2 =
Display 4	2 + 7 =	1 + 1 =	5 + 4 =	2 + 0 =	3 + 6 =	0 + 2 =	6 + 3 =	1 + 1 =
Display 5	2 + 3 =	1 + 1 =	5 + 0 =	0 + 2 =	3 + 2 =	2 + 0 =	2 + 3 =	1 + 1 =
Display 6	2 + 0 =	2 + 1 =	2 + 2 =	5 + 0 =	0 + 2 =	1 + 2 =	3 + 1 =	2 + 3 =
Display 7	6 + 3 =	4 + 4 =	5 + 2 =	5 + 1 =	3 + 2 =	1 + 3 =	2 + 0 =	1 + 0 =
Display 8	2 + 3 =	1 + 1 =	2 + 0 =	5 + 0 =	3 + 2 =	1 + 1 =	0 + 2 =	2 + 3 =

✤ Put a number on your calculator display, make up some clues and ask a friend to find your number.

Name ____________________

Calculator trail

A game for two players.

You will need: a counter and a calculator for each player.

✤ Choose a trail and put your counter on the 0.

✤ To move along the trail, at each place do a sum on your calculator to make the number shown in the next place. You cannot use the clear key.

✤ If you make a mistake, miss a turn.

✤ The first person to complete their trail is the winner.

0 2 5 6 9 11

0 3 7 8 10 12

✤ Design your own trails.

Name ______________

Addition bonds: 5 to 10

✤ Cut out these cards and use your calculator to help you to sort them into groups which have the same answers.

2 + 3 =	6 + 4 =	1 + 5 =	5 + 4 =
6 + 1 =	4 + 4 =	8 + 1 =	4 + 3 =
4 + 1 =	5 + 5 =	0 + 5 =	2 + 7 =
3 + 3 =	5 + 3 =	3 + 4 =	4 + 2 =
3 + 7 =	3 + 2 =	1 + 7 =	6 + 3 =
2 + 6 =	5 + 2 =	2 + 8 =	2 + 4 =

Name ____________________

House numbers

✤ Use your calculator to help you to write some addition sums in the windows with answers that match the number on the door. One window has been done for you.

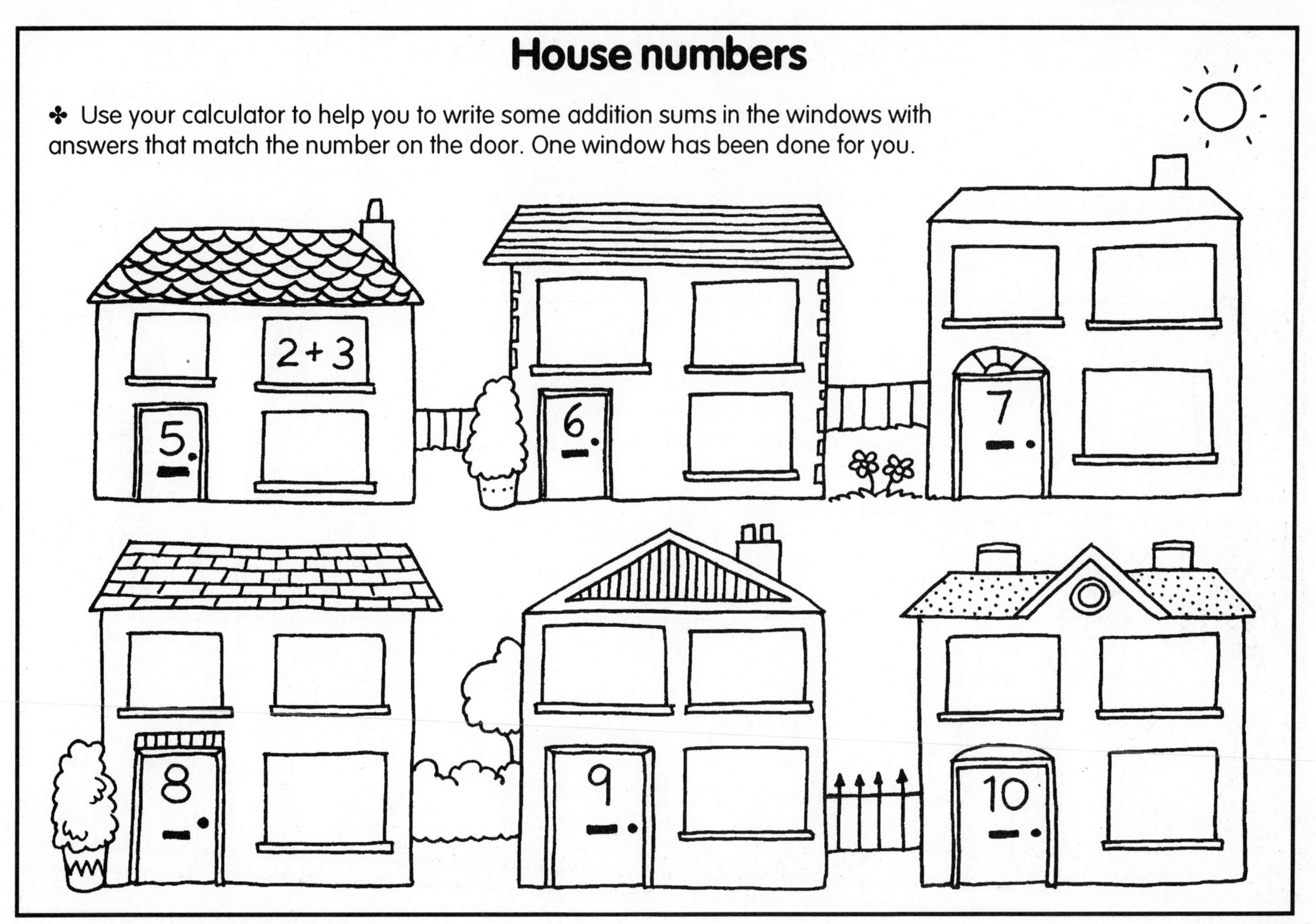

Name ____________________

Skittles

A game for two players.

You will need: 20 counters, two dice and a calculator.

✤ Choose your set of skittles.

✤ Take turns to throw both the dice. Add or subtract the numbers thrown using your calculator to find a number on a skittle. Cover the skittle with a counter.

✤ If you throw a double you may have another turn.

✤ The winner is the one who covers all their skittles first.

Name ____________________

Where am I going?

✤ Squirrel has a map and a route. Use your calculator to find out where the squirrel is going.

Route

3 + 3 =
3 + 4 =
7 − 1 =
2 + 0 =
5 − 4 =
4 − 2 =
7 − 6 =
9 − 5 =
6 + 2 =
5 + 4 =
3 + 5 =

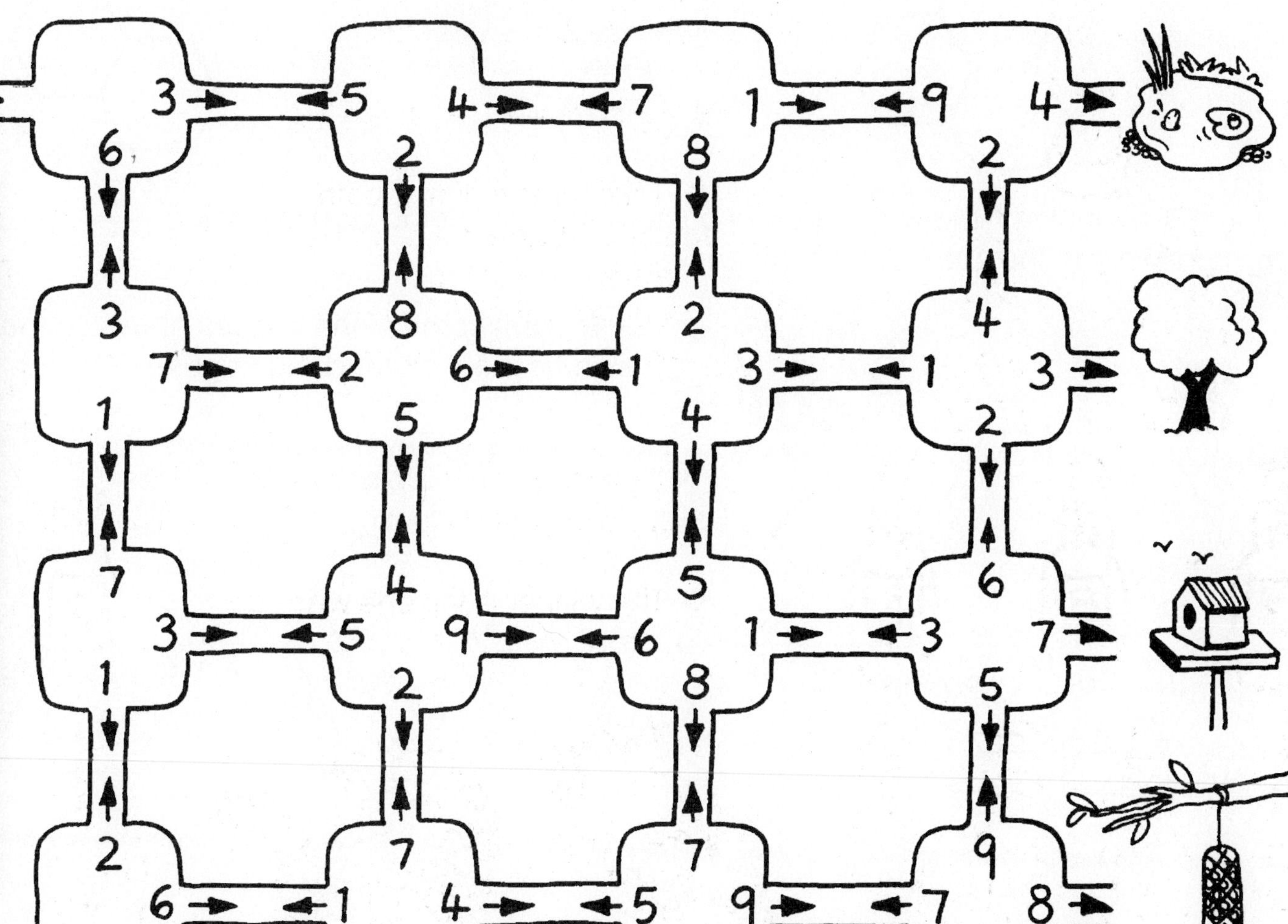

Name ____________________

Trihexes

Three regular hexagons can be fitted together like this:

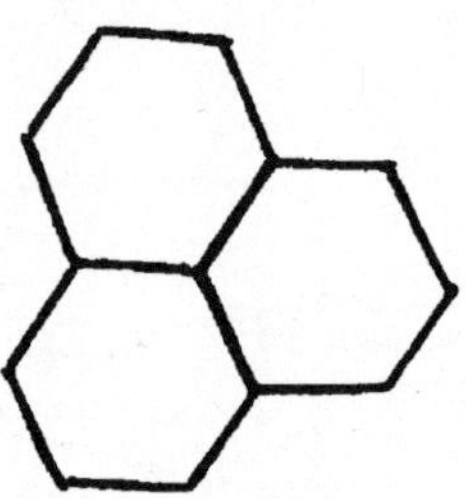

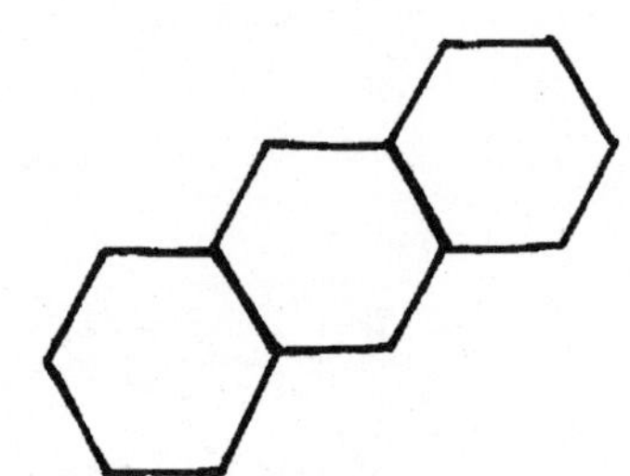

✤ Cut out the hexagons below and use your calculator to work out the answers to the questions on the edges.

✤ Form some of the shapes above so that answers which are the same meet on touching edges.

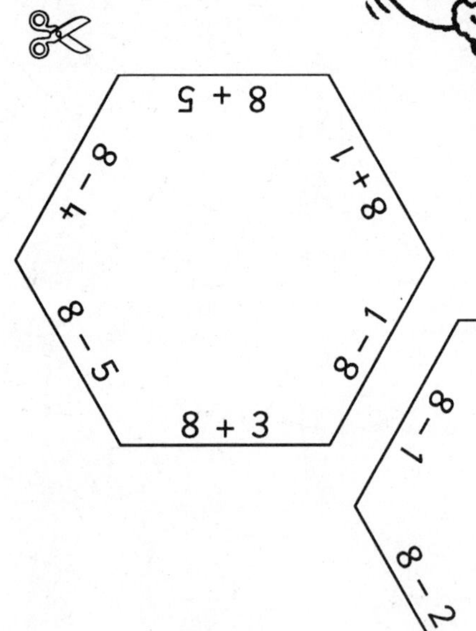

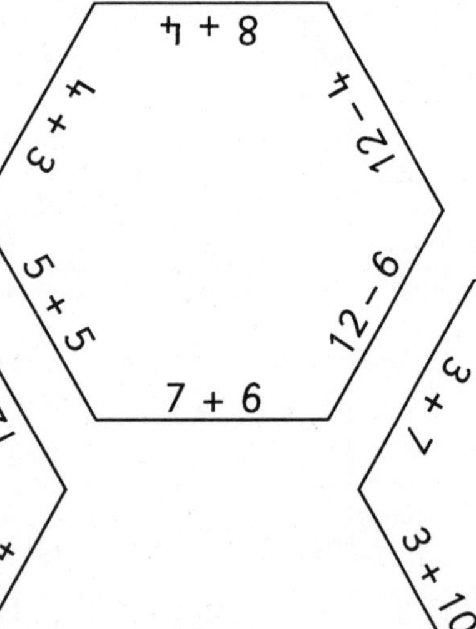

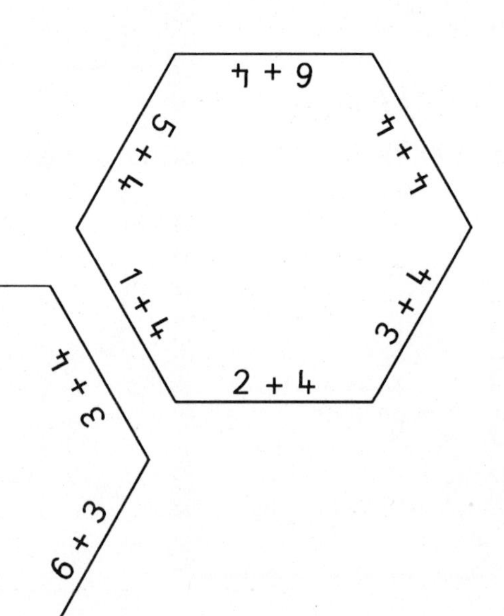

Name ____________________

How old is the tortoise?

✤ Use a calculator to work out the answers to the questions on the tortoise.

✤ If the answers are:

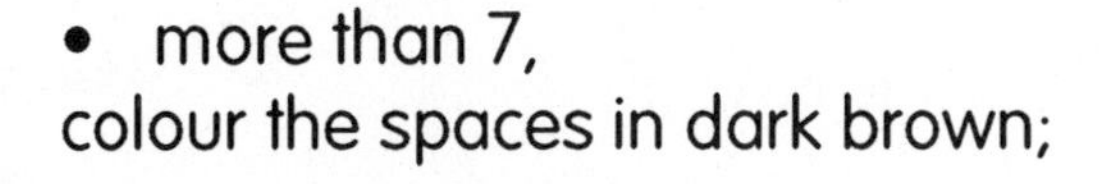

- more than 7,
colour the spaces in dark brown;

- equal to 7,
colour the spaces in red;

- less than 7,
colour the spaces in light brown.

✤ Read the age of the tortoise. You will find it on the shell.

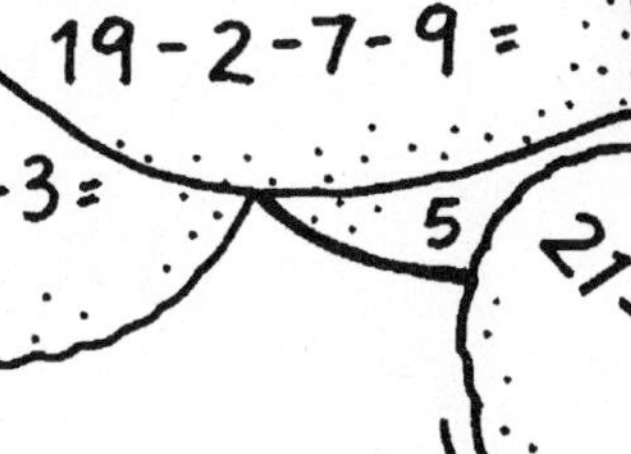

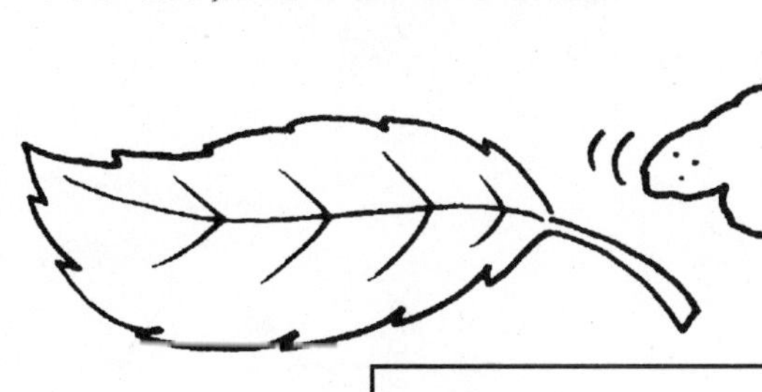

The tortoise is ____________ years old.

Name ______________

From here to there

✤ There are lots of ways in which you can change 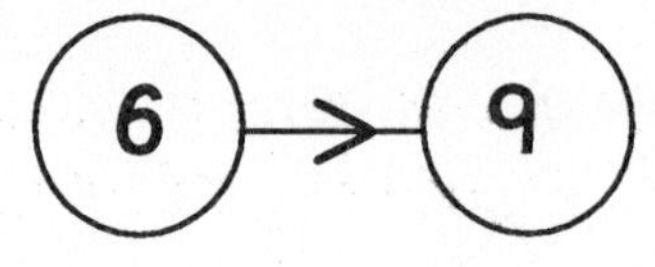

on your calculator.

You can enter **6 + 3 =**
or **6 + 1 + 2 =**
or **6 + 4 − 1 =**

✤ Find as many ways as you can to make these changes:

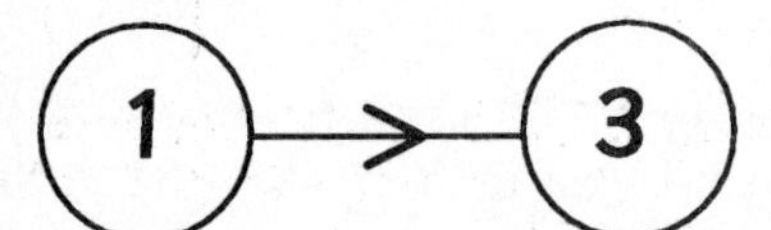

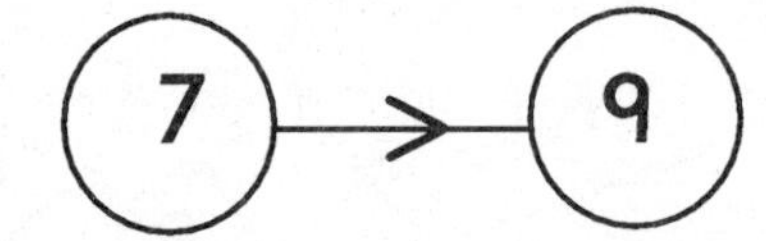

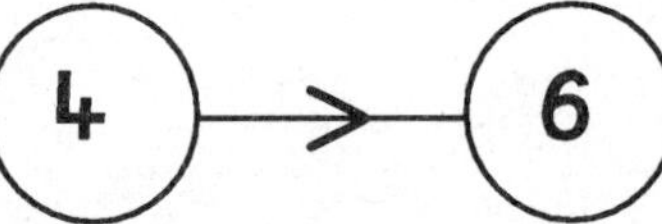

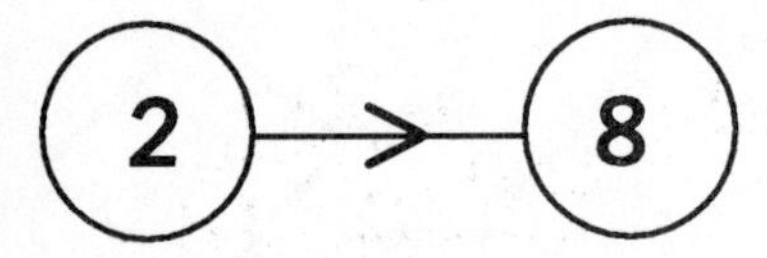

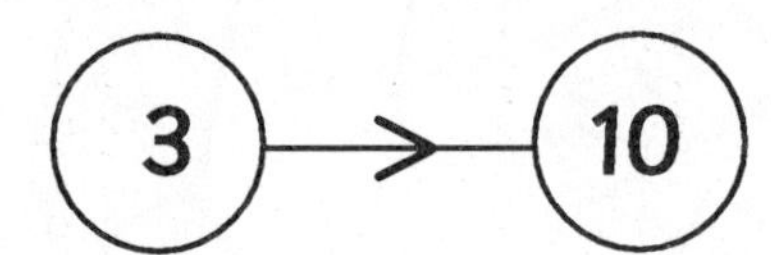

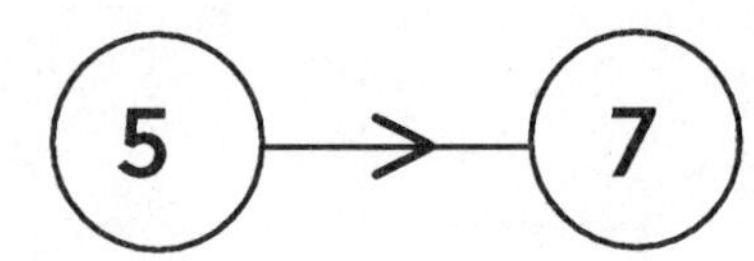

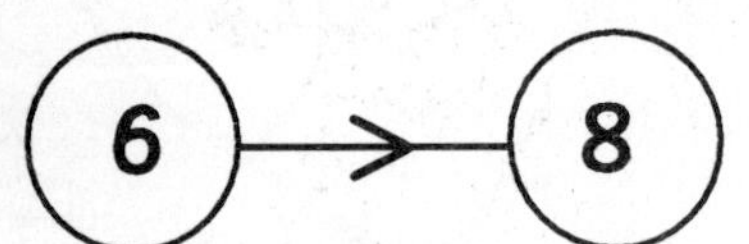

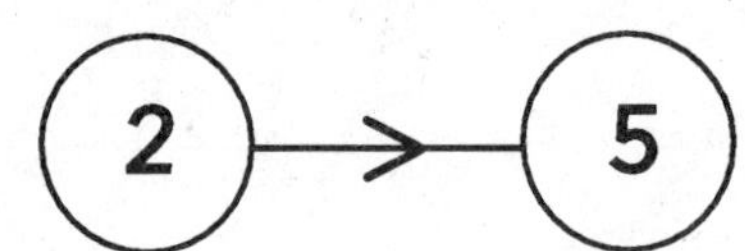

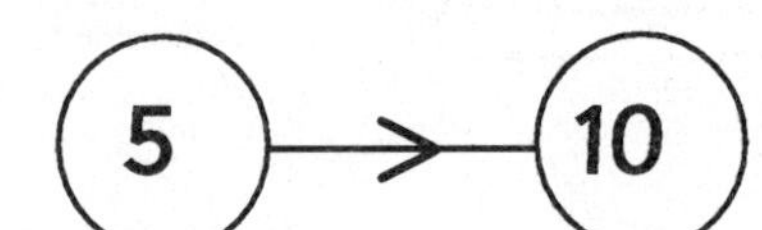

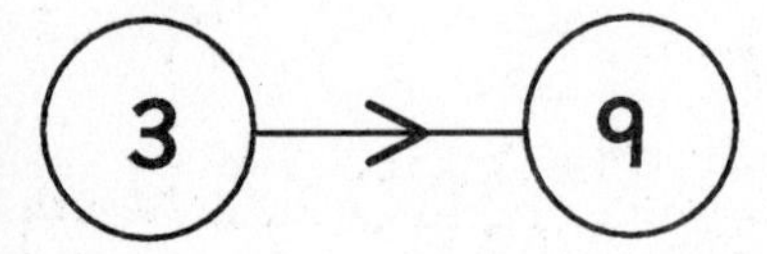

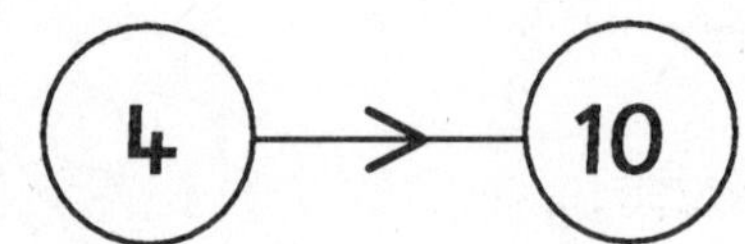

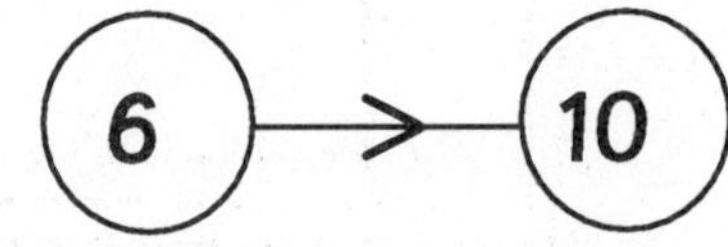

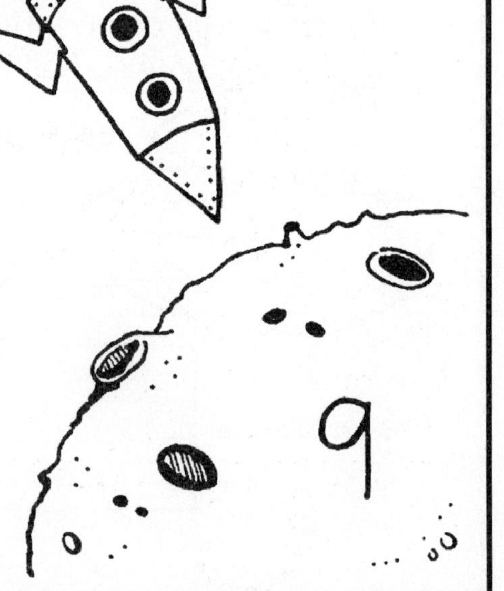

See-saw sums

✤ Put numbers into the boxes so that each see-saw balances and each pair of numbers add up to the number in the log. Use your calculator to help you.

Name ____________________

Triangle totals

✤ Use your calculator to help you to put numbers at the corners of each triangle so that the total of the three corner numbers is the same as the number inside.

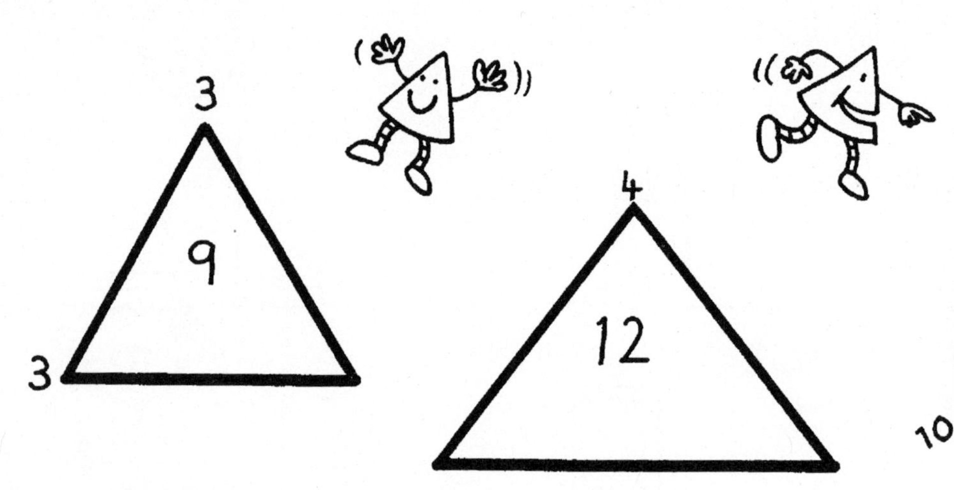

30
10

5
6
18
7

27

✤ Now draw some triangle totals of your own.

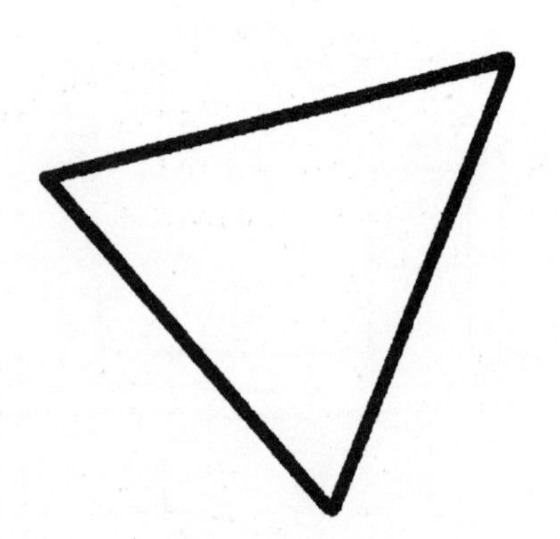

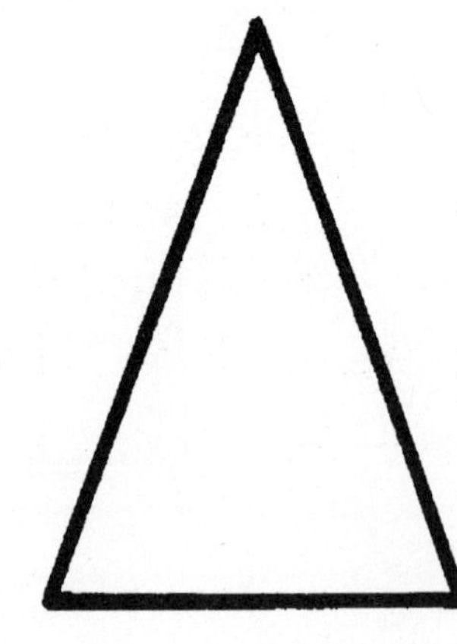

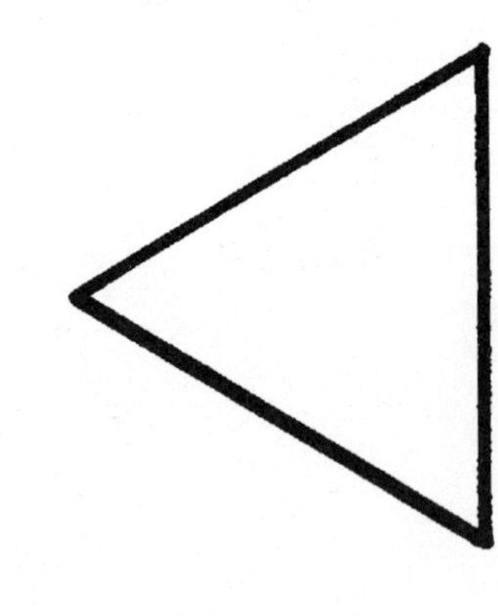

Name ____________________

Magic constant

✣ Clear your calculator and enter these keystrokes: [5] [+] [+] [=] [0]

- Enter 2 and press [=]. Write down what appears on your display.
- Enter 4 and press [=]. Write down what appears on your display.
- Enter 7 and press [=]. Write down what appears on your display.

✣ Using the same magic constant, what numbers would you have to enter so that these numbers appear on your display:

- 8? • 12? • 17? • 55? • 88? • 120?

✣ Try entering this magic constant: [9] [+] [+] [=] [0]

See what happens when you enter a number and press [=].

✣ Try entering this magic constant: [7] [–] [–] [4] [=] [0]

Then enter 12 and press [=]. Write down what appears on your display.

Try some other numbers.

✣ Explore some other constants. Try them on your friends.

Name ____________________

More than, less than

You will need: the word cards below, some number cards and a calculator.

✤ Deal a card on to each of the places shown.

✤ Choose the correct word card.

✤ Use the calculator to calculate the number to make the sentence correct.

For example: 6 is 3 more than 3

Number card

is

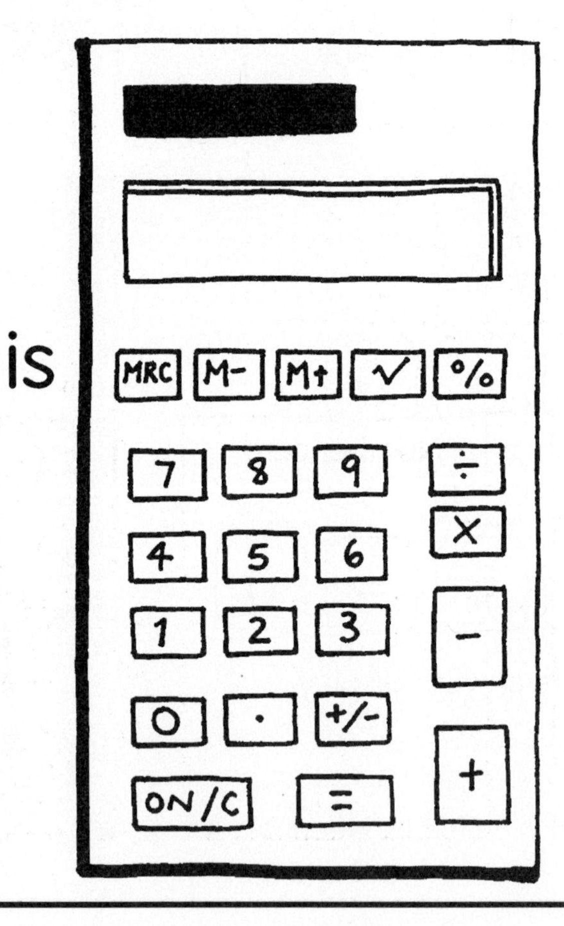

Word card

Number card

less than

more than

Three in a row

A game for two players.

You will need: eight counters each, the 1 to 6 number cards and a calculator.

✤ Spread out the number cards.

✤ Take turns to choose two number cards.

✤ Add the numbers. Use your calculator to help you. Then put your cards back.

✤ If the answer is on a free square, claim it with a counter. If the answer is already covered, do nothing and let the other player have a go.

✤ The winner is the first player to get three counters in a row.

10	3	9
4	11	5
8	6	7

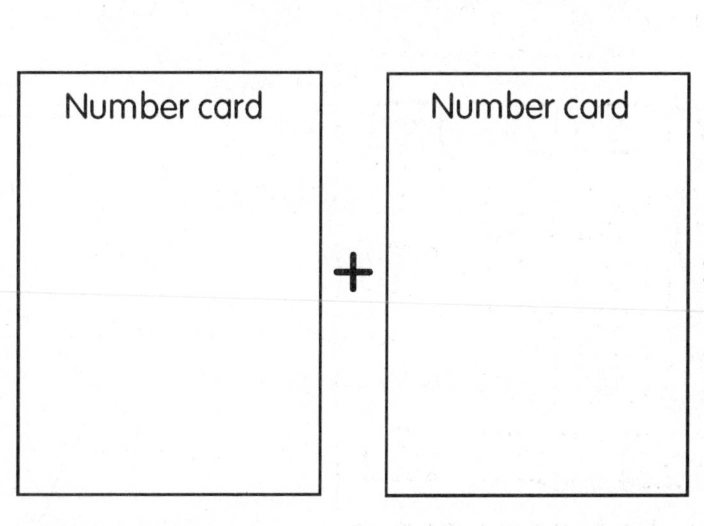

Name ____________

Words to add
✤ Use your calculator to add up the numbers written in each cloud. Check your result with the check total.
ten six two nine four
Check total: 31
two seven two three four
Check total: 18
eight one seven ten two
Check total: 28
four one two three five
Check total: 15
eight seven nine six
Check total: 30
nine one three nine five
Check total: 27
✤ Design your own set of word clouds and test them on a friend.

Deal a difference

A game for two players.

You will need: the 0 to 17 number cards, a pencil and a calculator.

✣ Choose who will be Player 1 and who will be Player 2.

✣ Shuffle the cards and deal five number cards to each player.

✣ Player 1 places one of their cards face up. Then Player 2 places a card next to it, and says 'Higher!' or 'Lower!'

✣ The player with the higher card uses the calculator to work out the difference between the numbers on the cards and scores that many points.

✣ Player 1 now places another card, and says 'Higher!' or 'Lower!' again, and so on.

✣ The winner is the player with the highest total when all the cards have been used.

Player 1	**Player 2**
Number card	Number card

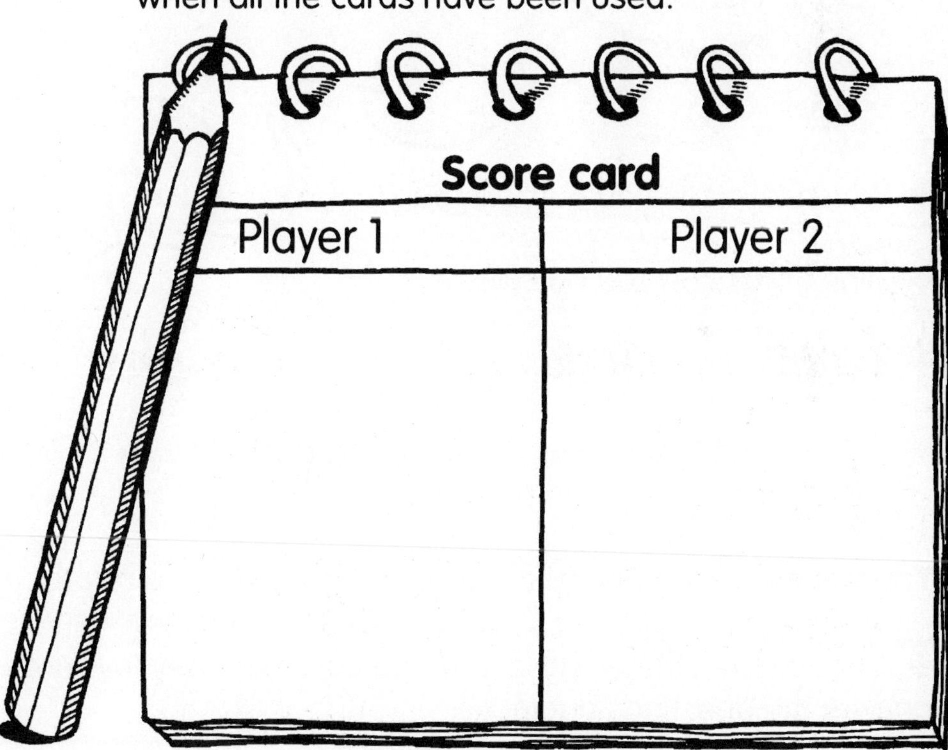

Name ____________________

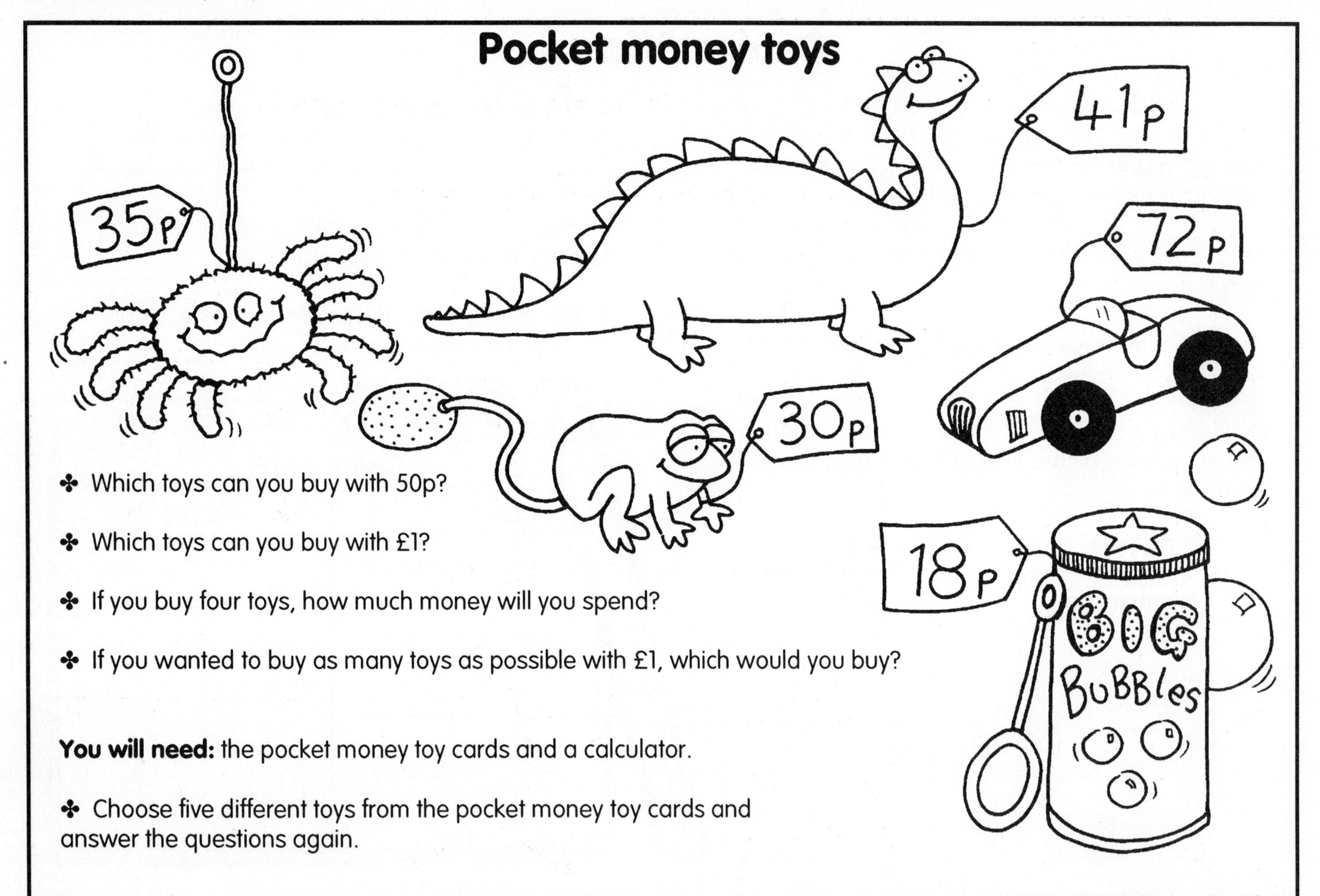

Pocket money toys

✤ Which toys can you buy with 50p?

✤ Which toys can you buy with £1?

✤ If you buy four toys, how much money will you spend?

✤ If you wanted to buy as many toys as possible with £1, which would you buy?

You will need: the pocket money toy cards and a calculator.

✤ Choose five different toys from the pocket money toy cards and answer the questions again.

Name ____________________

Star sums

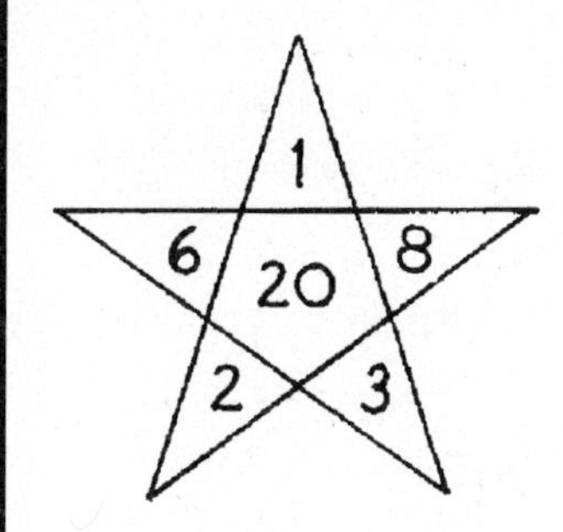

✤ Put five numbers in the points of the star so that their total is the same as the number in the middle.

✤ Use your calculator to make sure that the numbers are correct.

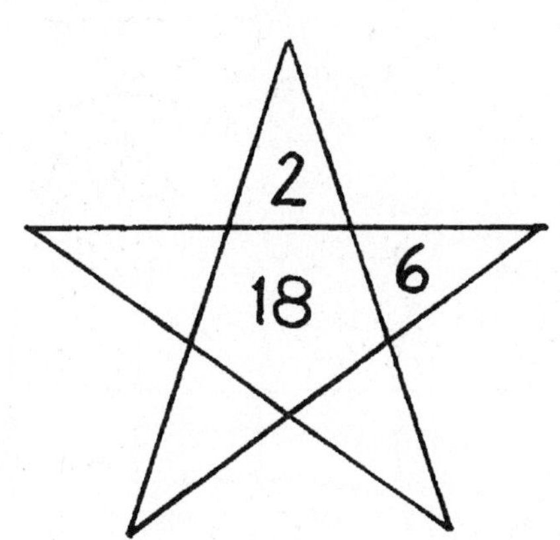

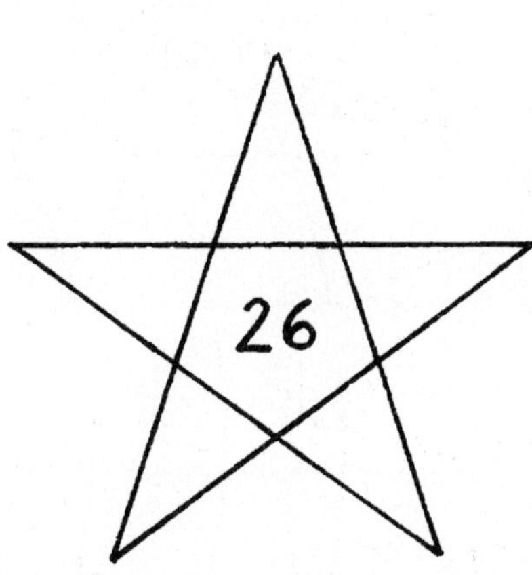

✤ Now make up some whole star sums of your own.

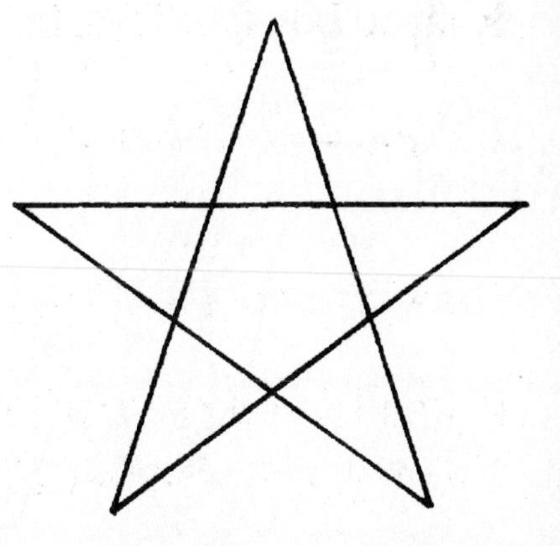

Name ____________________

Magic circle

In a magic circle, all the numbers in a ring (annulus) and all the numbers in a sector add up to the same number.

✤ Use your calculator to find out if this is a magic circle.

✤ Colour the number spaces in order: 1, 2, 3... and so on. Can you find any rules as to where to find the next number?

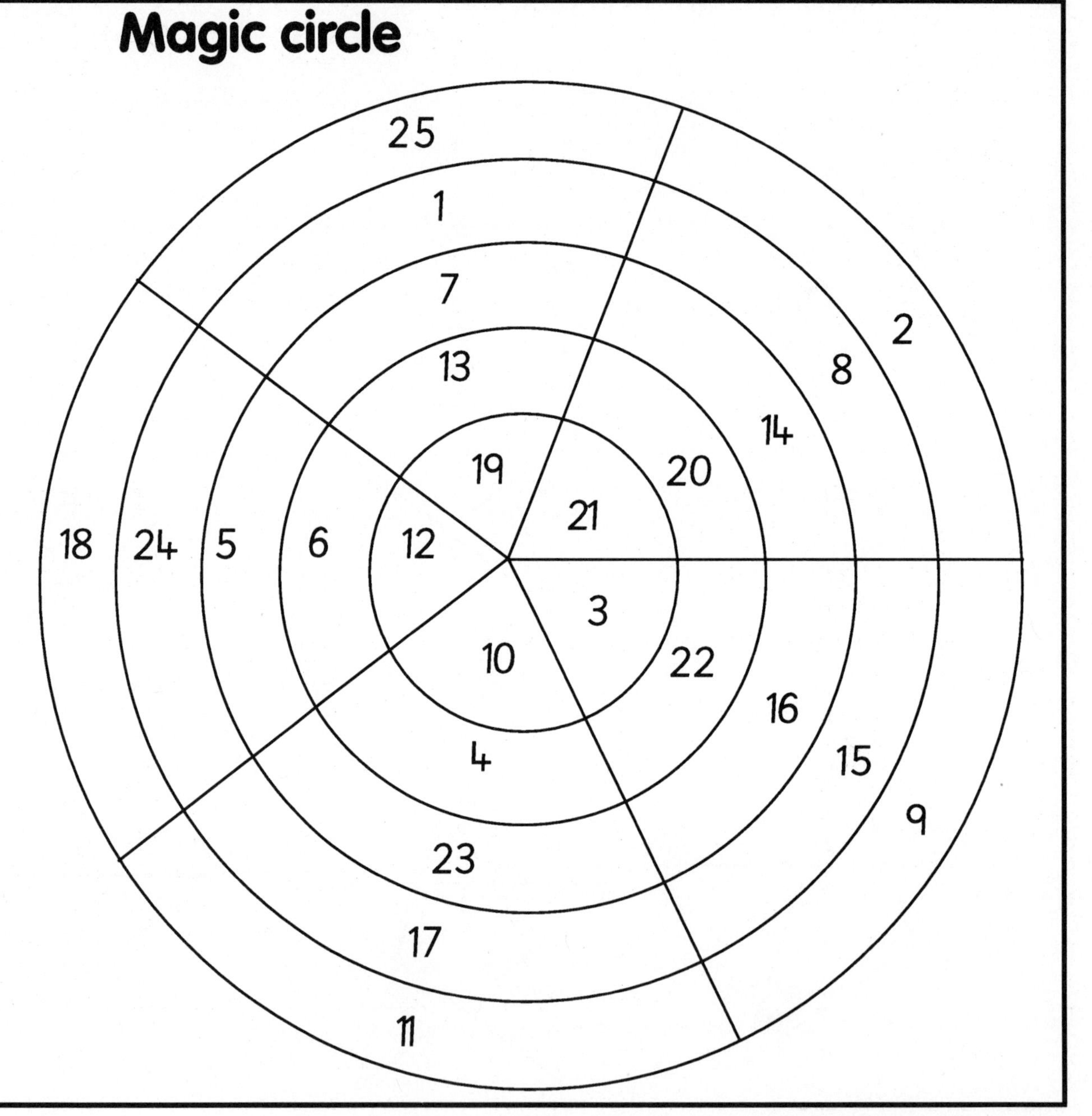

Name ____________________

Triangle jigsaw

- Cut out the four triangles opposite.
- Use your calculator to work out the addition sum on each edge.
- Put the four triangles together again, to make a large triangle, so that sides which touch have the same answer.
- How many different ways can you do this?

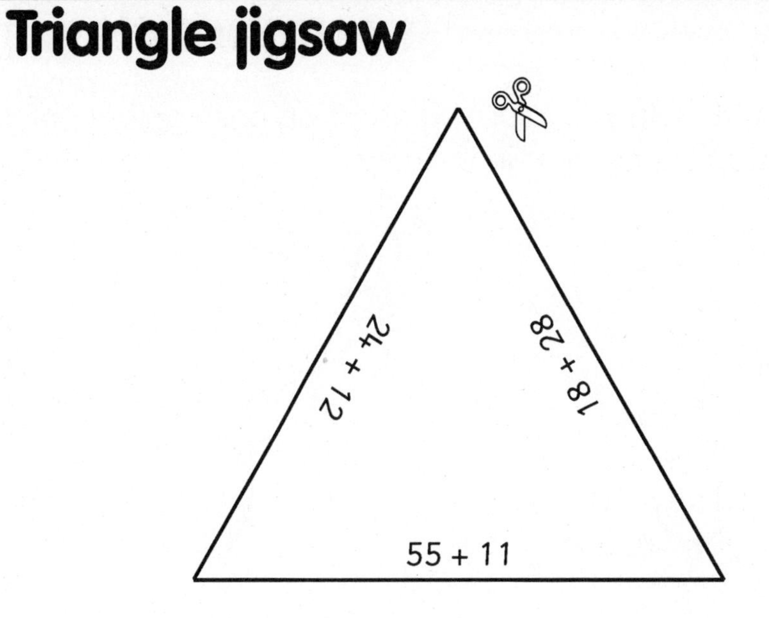

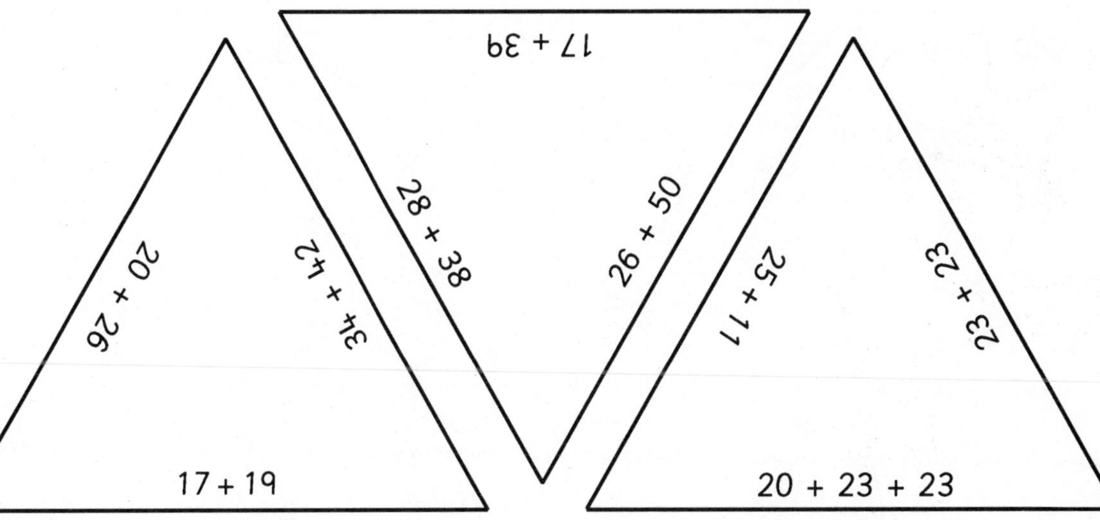

Name ____________

A number flower

✤ Use your calculator to help you to put numbers on each pair of petals so that their total is the same as the number in the centre.

Name ____________________

A 5s dot-to-dot

✤ Set up your calculator to count in 5s: C 5 + + = 0

As you press = find each number from the display on the diagram below and join the dots one at a time in the correct order.

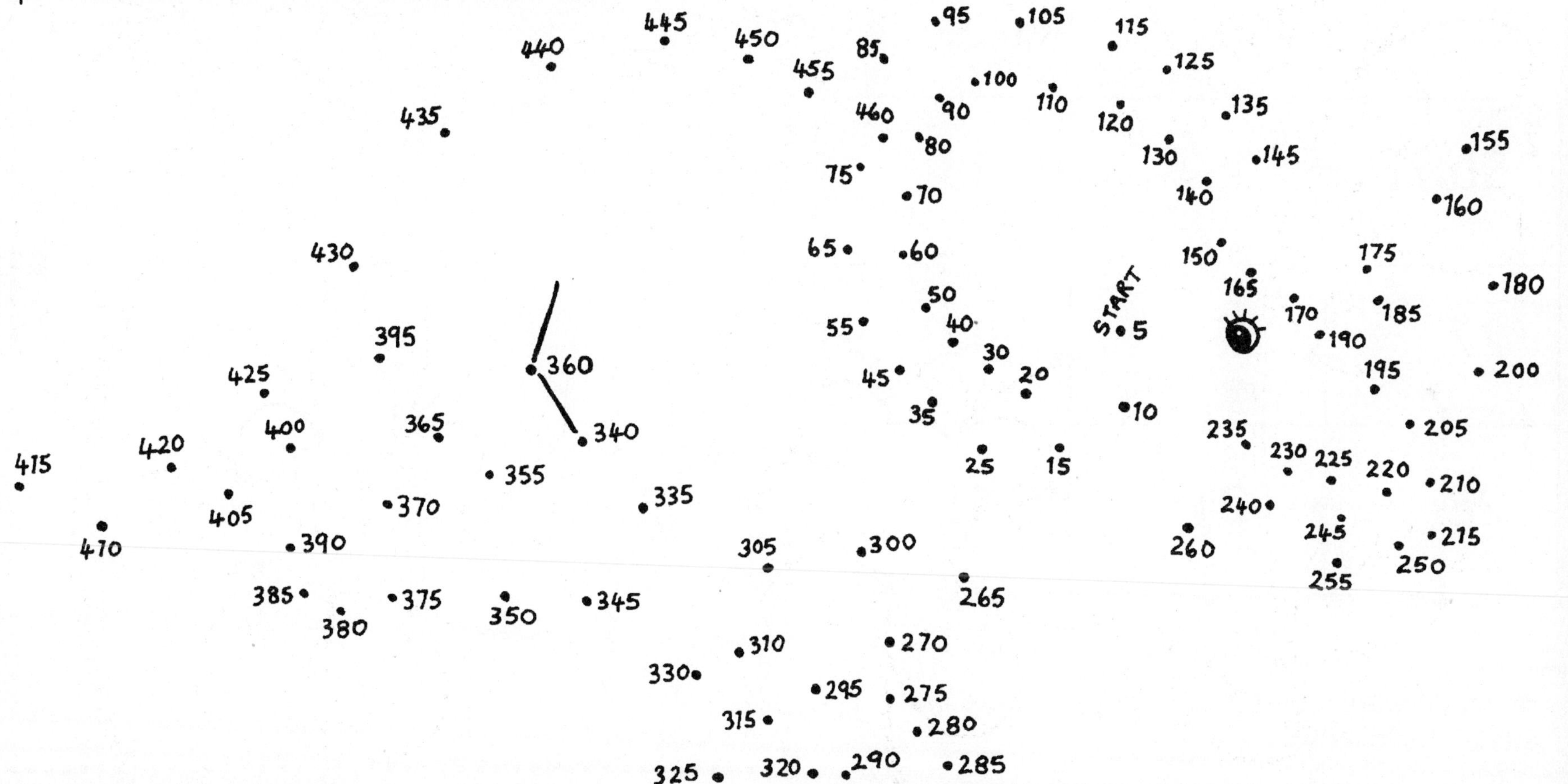

Number maze

✤ From the start, move through the maze in the direction of the arrows only; that is, right and down. For example: 16, 18, 12, 11.

✤ Add up the numbers as you move through. Use your calculator to help you. What totals do you get?

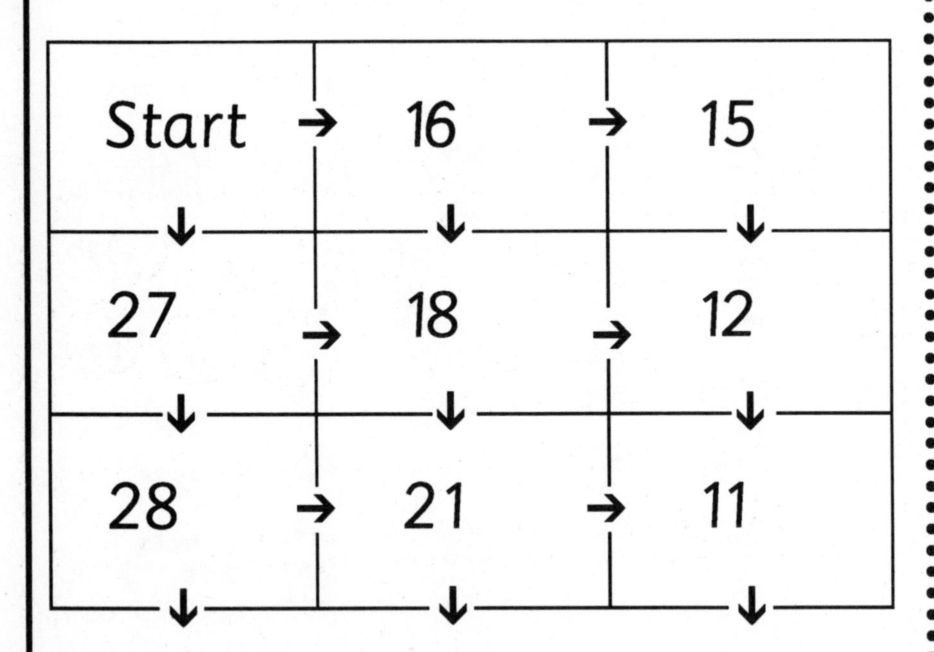

✤ Try different routes. How many totals are the same? Try to explain why.

✤ Now try to design your own maze of this size, so that at least three routes add up to 100. Continue on the back of this page.

Name ____________

Stars and circles

If a ◯ is worth 10 points and a ☆ is worth 15 points,

then this box:

is worth 60 points.

✤ Use your calculator to work out what each of these boxes is worth:

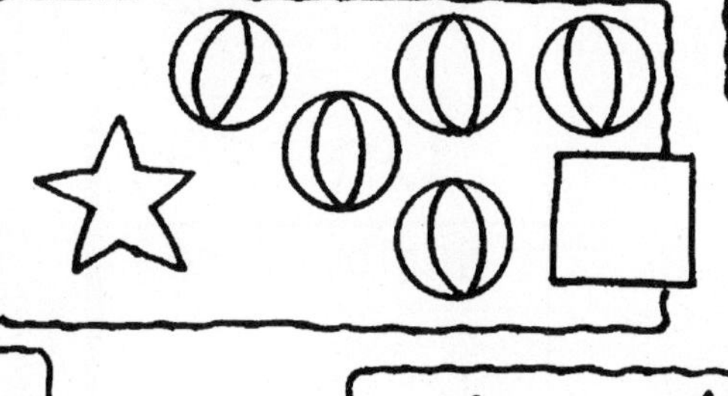

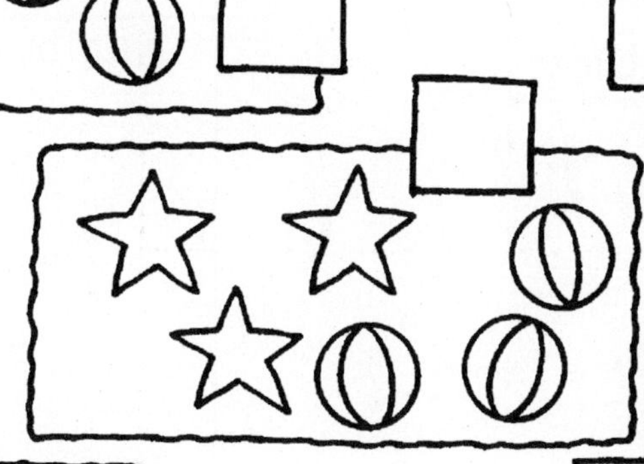

✤ Use your calculator to help you to design some boxes which are worth 150 points.

Name ____________________

Triple totals

You will need: two sets of the 1 to 9 number cards, a pencil, paper and a calculator.

✤ Shuffle the cards.

✤ Deal four of them on to the diagram opposite.

✤ Write down the three numbers you can make. Then use your calculator to add them together. For example:

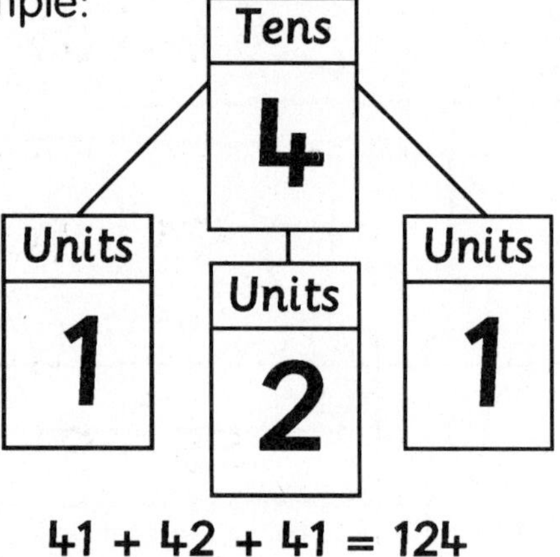

41 + 42 + 41 = 124

✤ Try this several times.

✤ Can you get exactly 100? Or 200? In how many ways can you do this?

✤ What is the largest number you can get?

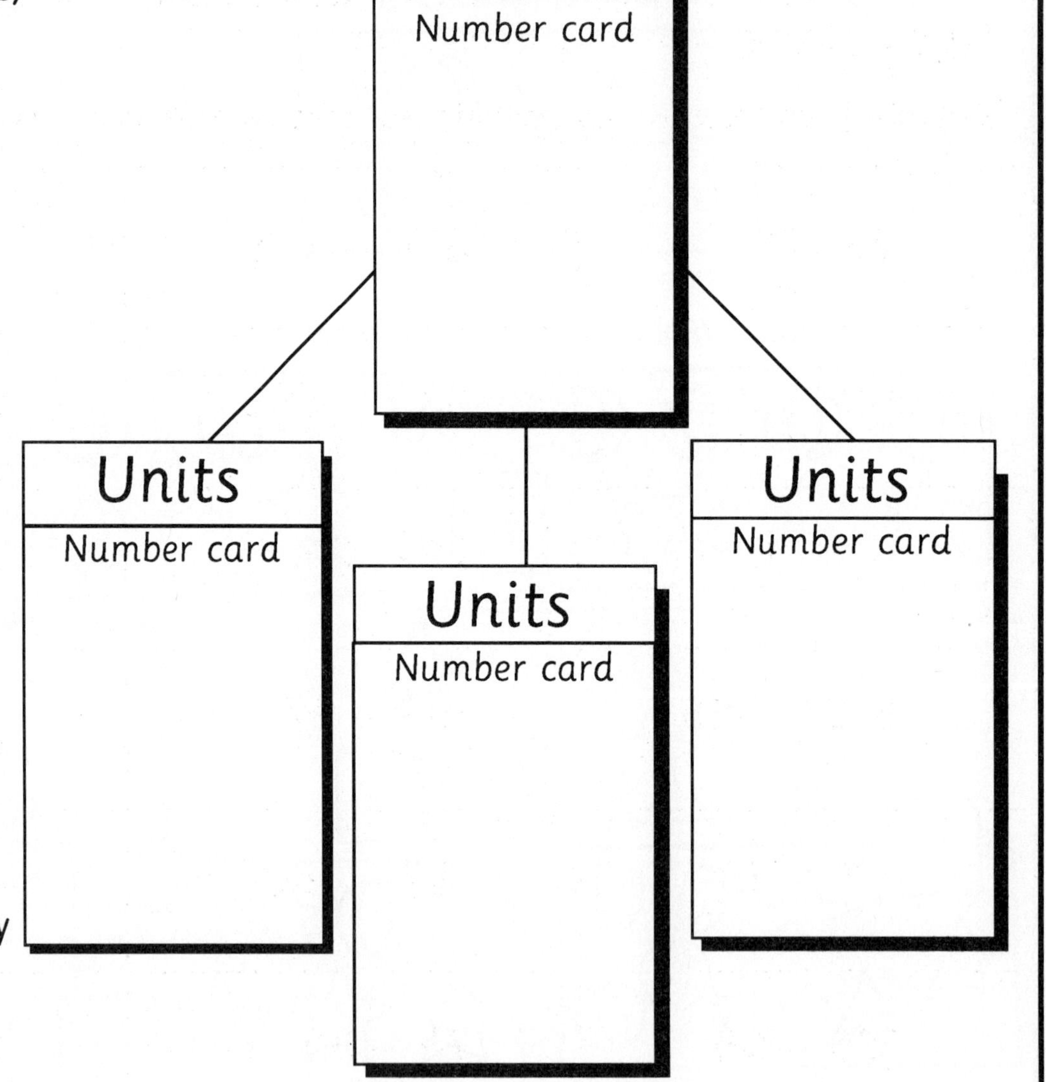

Name ____________________

Matching minus

✤ Cut out the cards below and use your calculator to help you to sort them into groups which have the same answers.

✤ What clues could you use to sort these cards without using a calculator?

23 – 17	376 – 355	117 – 80	496 – 409
416 – 329	635 – 593	216 – 169	86 – 65
47 – 10	76 – 29	276 – 189	613 – 607
516 – 495	103 – 97	105 – 63	56 – 9
176 – 129	187 – 150	166 – 145	495 – 453
136 – 49	75 – 33	153 – 147	227 – 190

Digit spinners

You will need: scissors, three cocktail sticks, a pencil, paper and a calculator.

✤ Cut out two of these spinners. Push a cocktail stick through the centre of each spinner.

✤ Spin both to make a two-digit number. Write the number down.

✤ Spin them again. Write down the new number.

✤ Use your calculator to add the two two-digit numbers.

✤ Try this 20 times. Are any of your results more than 100?

✤ Try this with all three spinners to generate pairs of three-digit numbers. Do you ever get a result which is more than 1000?

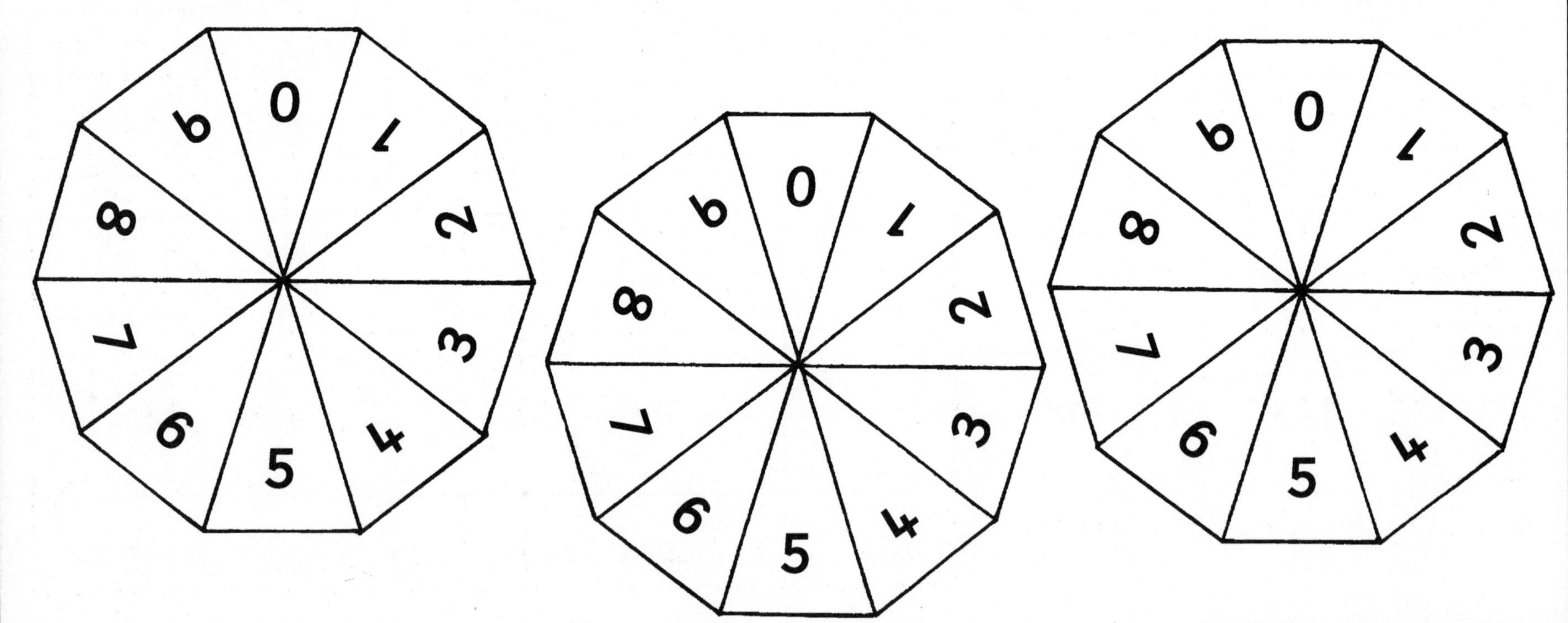

Name ____________________

Points for circles

If a circle is worth 24 points, then half a circle is worth half the 24 points and a quarter of a circle is worth a quarter of the 24 points.

For example:  is worth 24 + 12 + 6 = 42 points.

✤ Use your calculator to help you to work out what each of these boxes is worth:

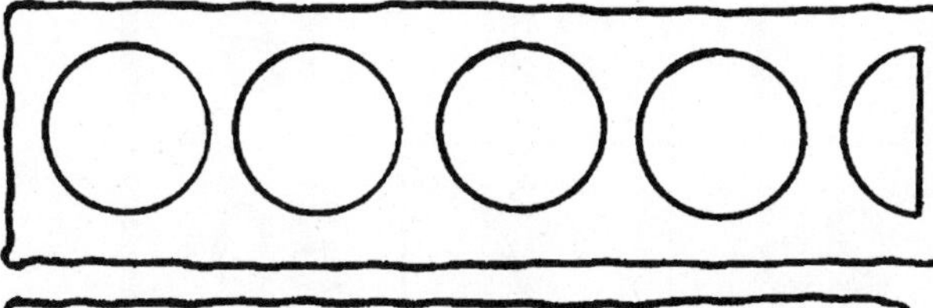

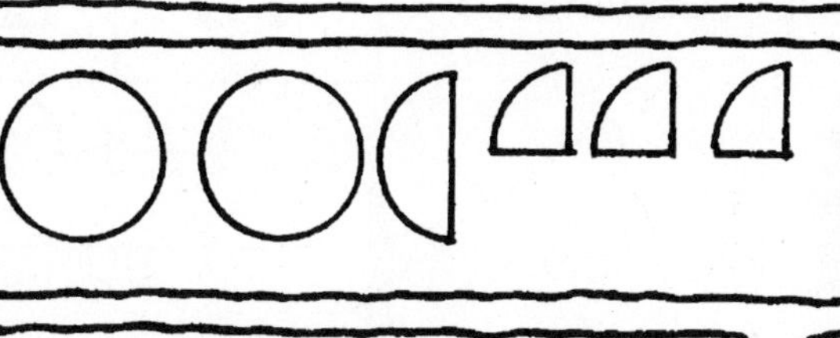

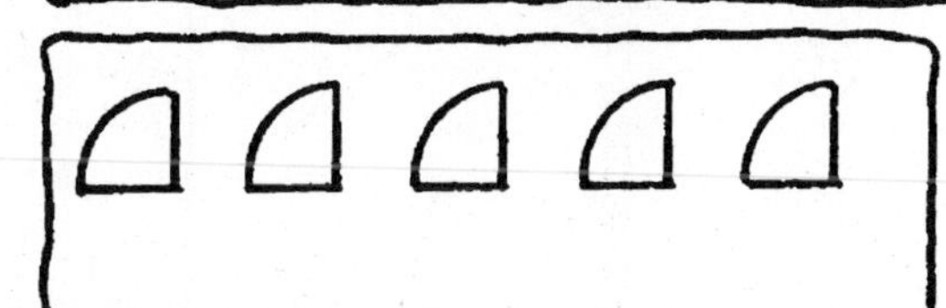

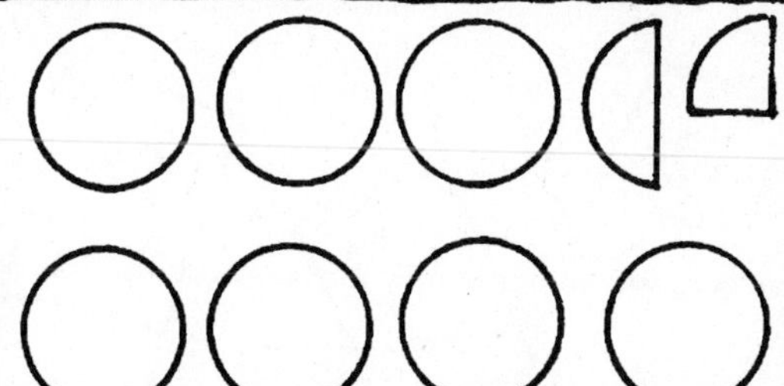

✤ Design some boxes worth 96 points.

Name ____________________

Lines of three

A game for two players.

You will need: about 20 counters each, a pencil, the 1 to 10 number cards and a calculator.

✣ Decide who will go first.

✣ Take turns to choose three number cards and use your calculator to find their total. If that number is free, place one of your counters over it.

✣ Each time you get a line of three, in any direction, tally it on the score card.

6	17	14	29	21
12	20	28	24	10
8	26	18	16	9
23	11	13	22	15
19	27	25	7	30

Score card

Player 1	Player 2

Name ____________________

How long is a line?

You will need: a ruler, a pencil and a calculator.

✤ Use the ruler to find the length of each line.

✤ Use your calculator to find which calculation in the table on the right matches the position and length of the line.

✤ Colour the box containing that calculation in the right colour.

✤ Now draw some lines for the other calculations.

Blue
0 1 2 3 4 5 6 7 8 9 10

Green
0 1 2 3 4 5 6 7 8 9 10

Yellow
0 1 2 3 4 5 6 7 8 9 10

Red
0 1 2 3 4 5 6 7 8 9 10

Brown
0 1 2 3 4 5 6 7 8 9 10

7 – 1 =	9 – 2 =
6 – 2 =	6 – 1 =
10 – 2 =	8 – 3 =
9 – 1 =	9 – 3 =
9 – 5 =	8 – 2 =

Name ____________

Line totals

✤ Read the number marked by each arrow and use your calculator to find the total for each number line. Your total should match the check total.

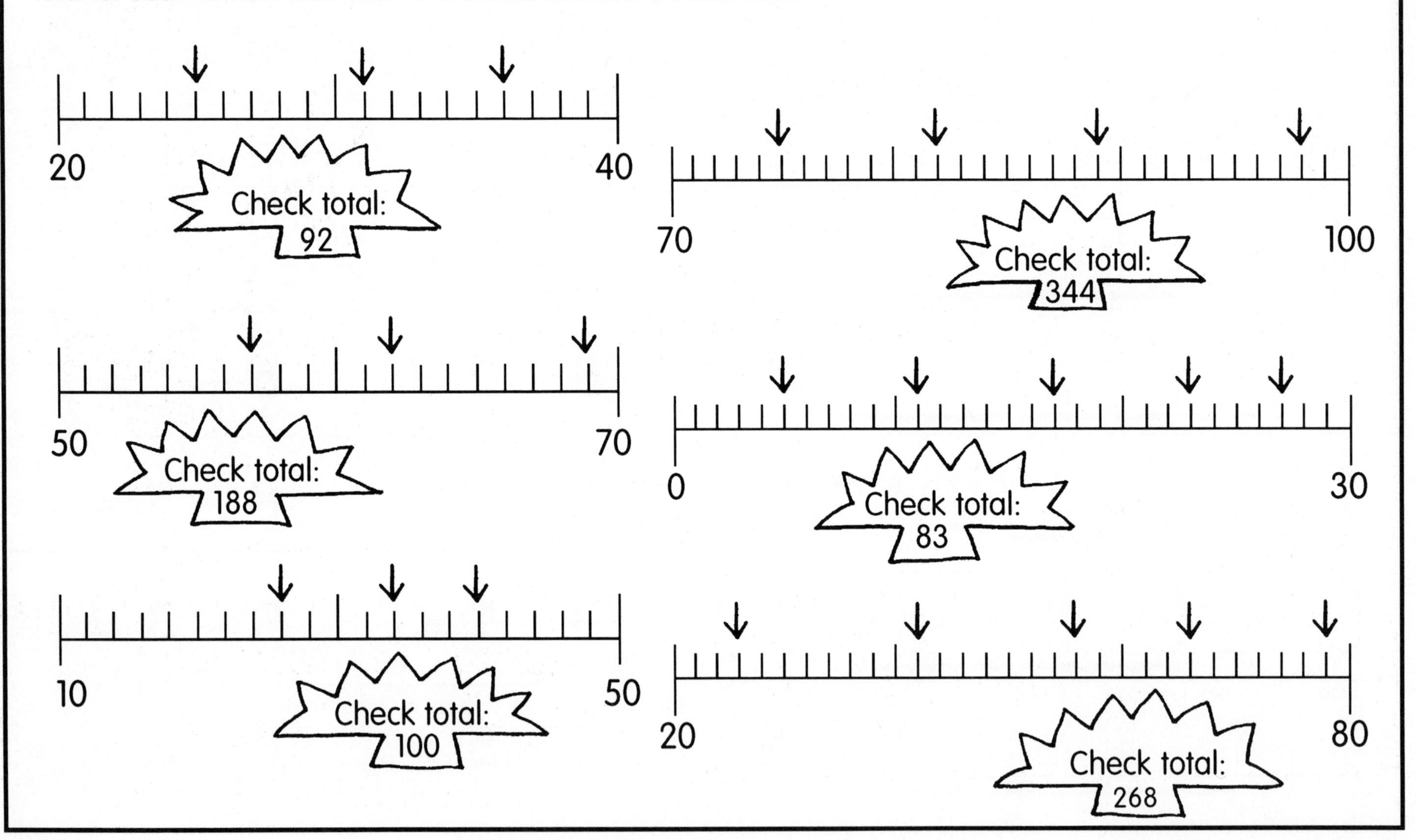

Name ____________________

Tens and units words to add

✤ Use your calculator to add up the numbers written in each cloud. Check each result with the check total.

thirty ninety eleven
twenty-two twenty-nine

Check total: 182

twenty-five
thirty-one sixteen
fifty thirteen

Check total: 135

eighty-two one
nineteen
fifty-one thirty-one

Check total: 184

eighty-one eleven
ninety-four
seventeen sixteen

Check total: 219

forty twelve
twenty-two thirteen
sixty-two

Check total: 149

✤ Write out some clouds whose totals are 509.

Name ____________________

Memory trail

- Clear the **memory** on your calculator by pressing: MRC MRC C

  or (perhaps): MC C

- Make this sequence of keystrokes: 5 M+ 3 M+

- What is shown on the calculator display?
- What do you think is in the memory?
- Press MRC to find out.

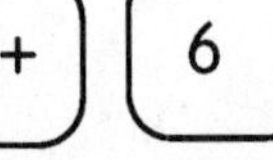

- Clear the memory before you try each of these key sequences. Predict what is in the memory before you press MRC.

Key sequence	I predict	MRC
4 M+ 3 M+ 3 M+		
9 M+ 6 M– 2 M+		
8 M+ 5 M+ 6 M–		

Key sequence	I predict	MRC
14 M+ 7 M+ 7 M+		
16 M+ 6 M– 6 M–		
1 M– 19 M+ 3 M–		

- Design some key sequences using M+ and M–, where 20 will be the result.

Name ____________

How long are the pencils?

✤ Measure all these pencils.

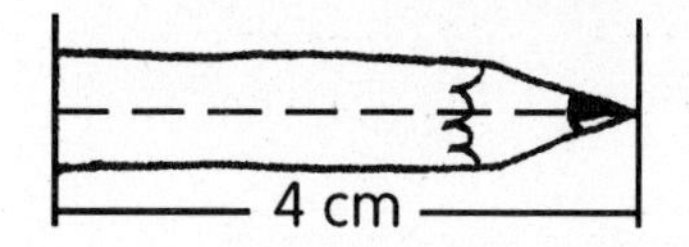

✤ Which two pencils, joined end to end in a straight line, would make a length of more than 18cm? Use your calculator to help you find out.

✤ Is it possible to make a length of less than 12cm with two pencils? How?

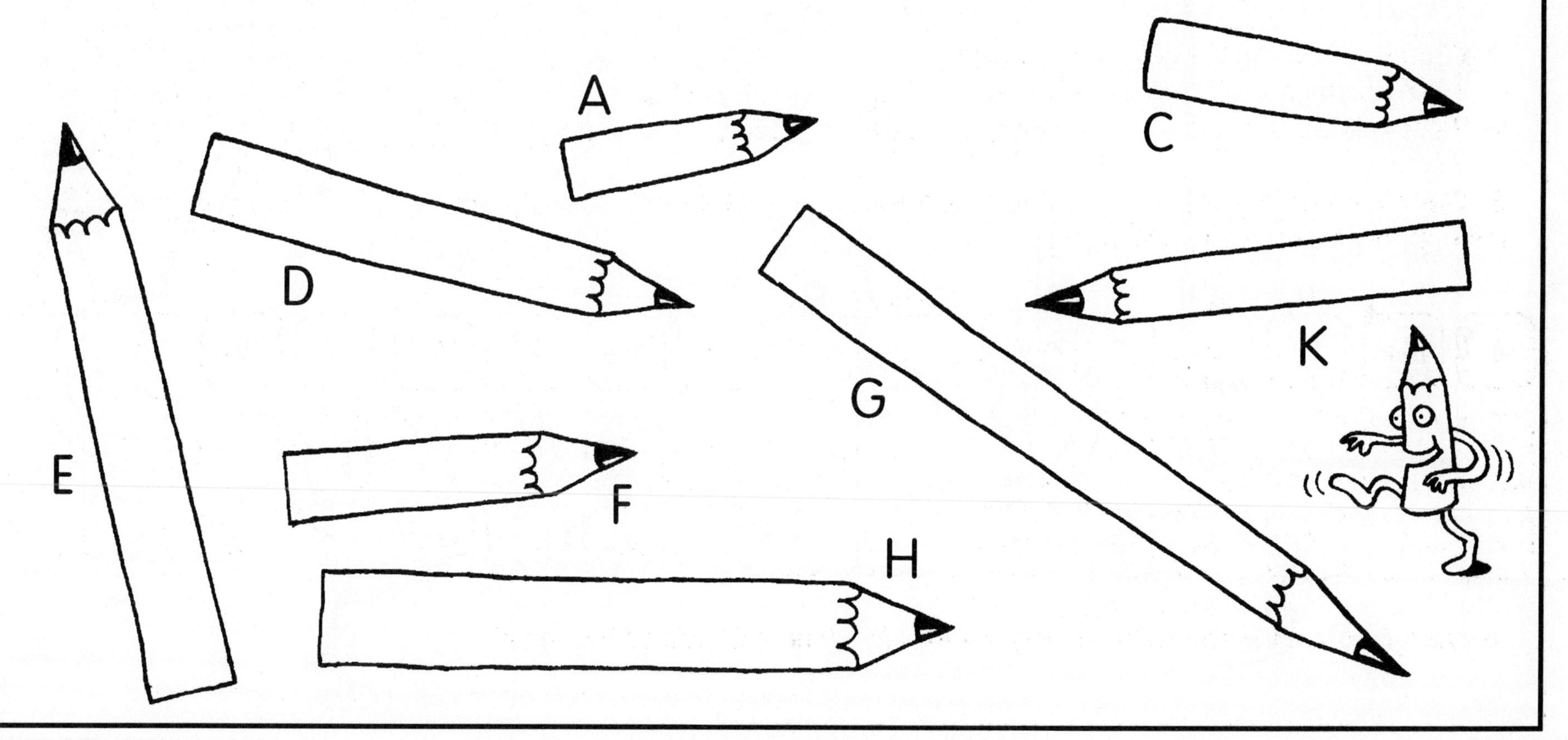

Name ____________________

Going visiting

✣ If the hedgehog follows the route below, who will it visit?

✣ Use your calculator to work out the answers to the sums for the route and follow the numbers on the map.

Route

12 – 2 =
23 – 6 =
5 × 5 – 2 =
4 × 5 – 1 =
60 ÷ 2 – 1 =
7 × 7 + 0 =
55 ÷ 5 =
132 ÷ 6 =

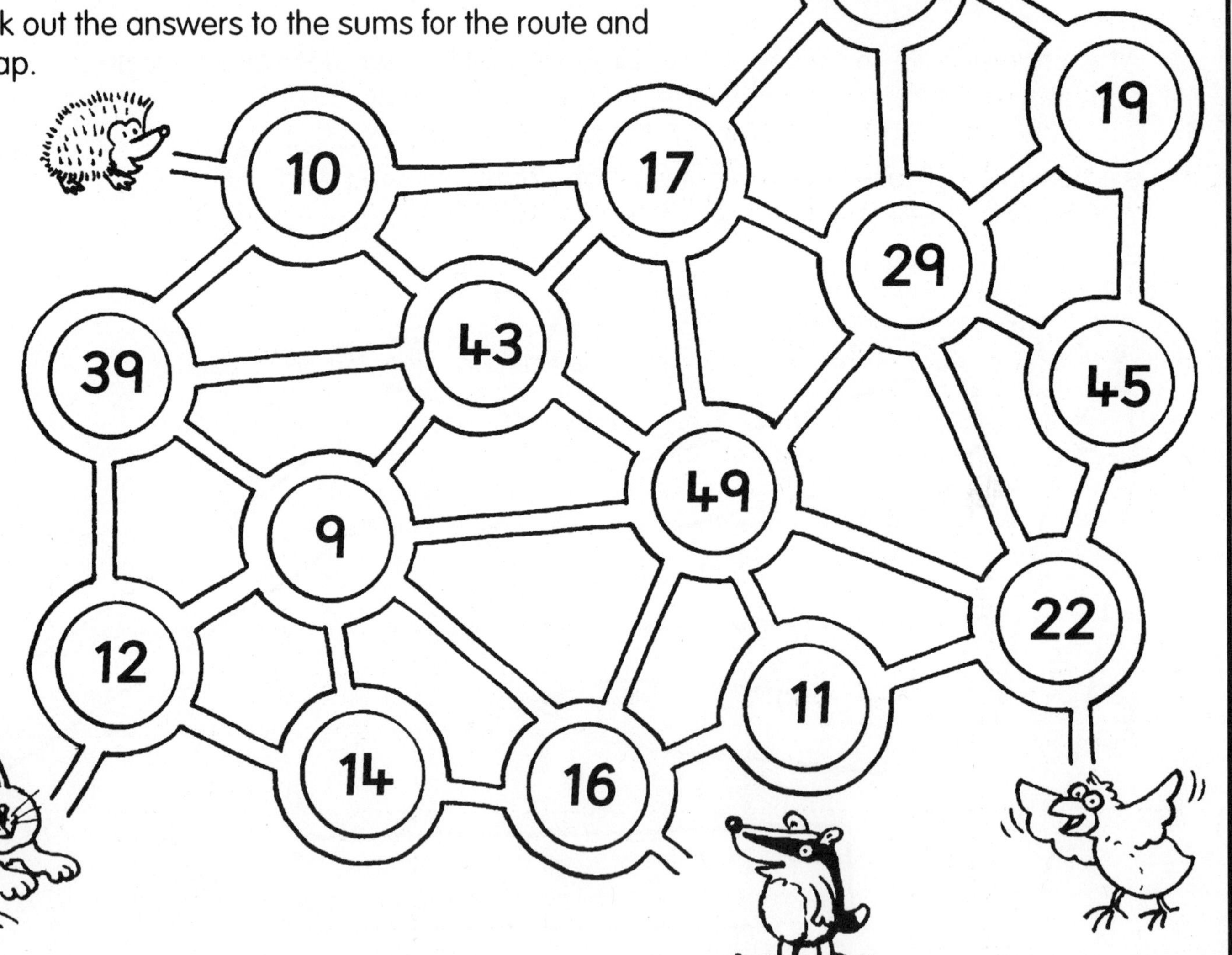

Name ____________________

Number cubes

- ✤ Carefully, cut out the cube nets below and make up the cubes.
- ✤ Is there anything special about the arrangement of the numbers on each cube?

- ✤ Throw all the dice.
- ✤ Look at the four numbers on the top faces of the cubes.
- ✤ Use your calculator to work out the total of the four numbers.
- ✤ Try this lots of times. Work out all the possible totals with these four dice.

- ✤ If the numbers are arranged into two two-digit numbers, what are the possible totals?
- ✤ What are the possible differences between the two two-digit numbers?

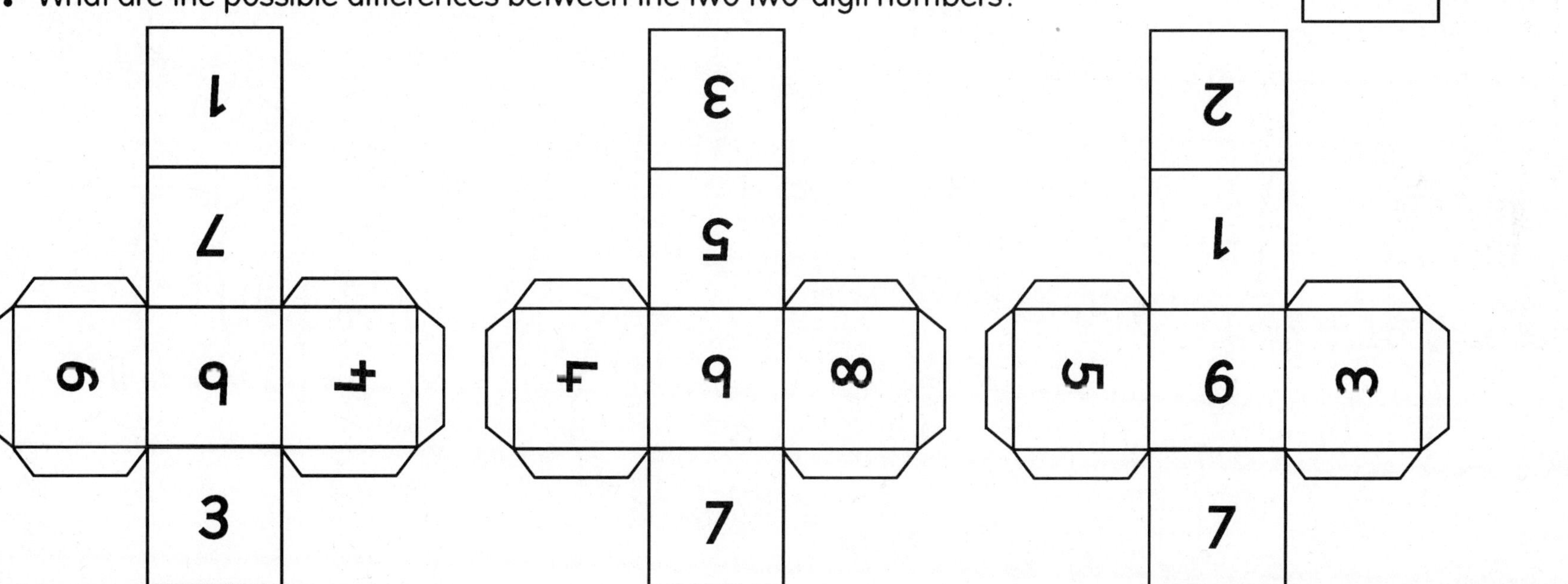

Calculatorpedes

A game for two players.

You will need: the three digit spinners, and a counter and a calculator each.

✤ Choose your calculatorpede. Put your counter on its head.

✤ Take turns to use the three digit spinners to give you three numbers. Use any operations you like to calculate the first number on your calculatorpede from the three digits.
For example, if you spin 6, 3 and 9 and you need 27, you can get 27 by doing $6 \times 3 + 9 =$.

✤ Next turn spin another three digits and calculate the next number.

✤ When you have completed each calculation, move your counter on to that segment of the calculatorpede. The first player to reach the tail is the winner.

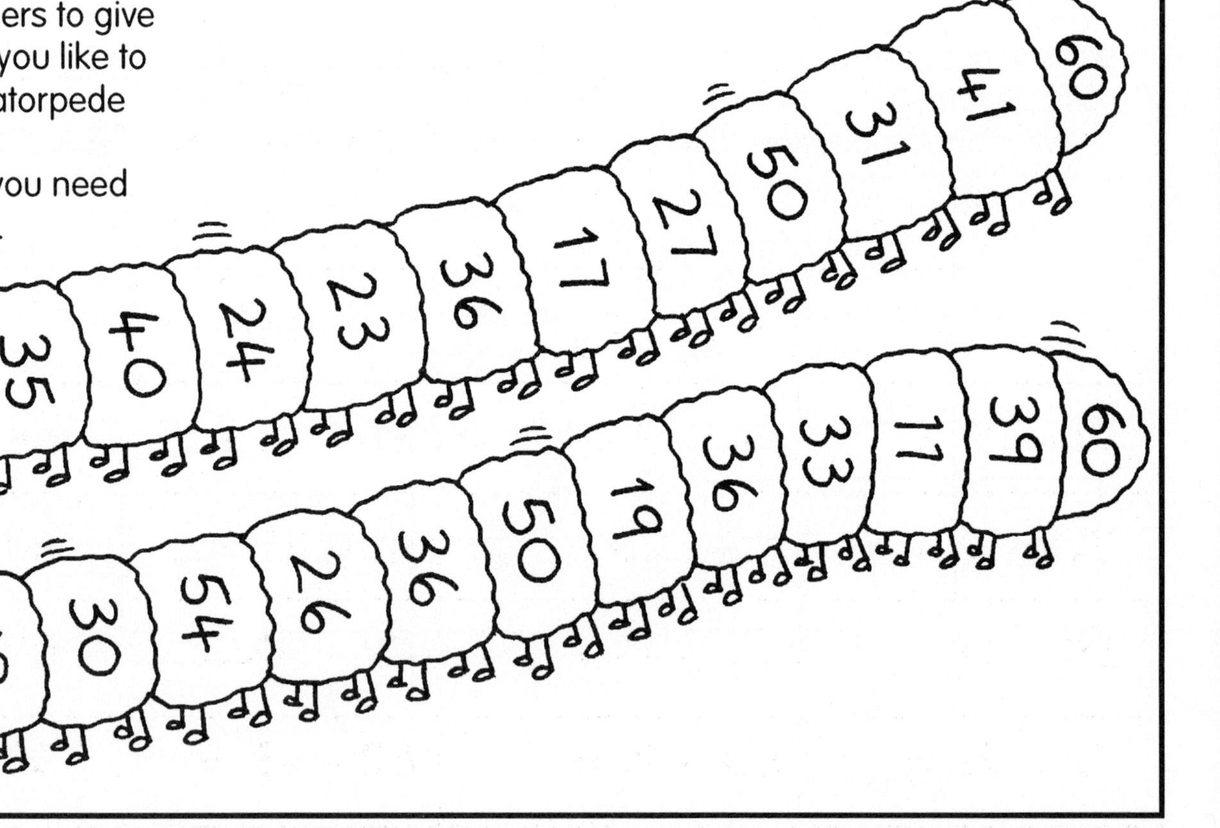

Name ____________________

Three together

A game for two players.

You will need: two different coloured pencils and a calculator.

✤ Choose who will go first.

✤ Take turns to choose a calculation, work out the answer on the calculator and mark a cross in the correct place on the number line.

✤ The winner is the first player to get three crosses together in their colour.

30 ———————————— 40 ———————————— 50

71 – 27 =	54 – 5 =	56 – 18 =	68 – 27 =	89 – 50 =
84 – 53 =	72 – 26 =	91 – 51 =	98 – 62 =	49 – 16 =
59 – 17 =	79 – 49 =	67 – 32 =	81 – 38 =	64 – 19 =
75 – 28 =	50 – 16 =	82 – 45 =	39 – 7 =	92 – 44 =

Totally amazing

✤ How many routes are there through this maze? Use your calculator to find the totals of the numbers you pass through on each route.

✤ Do any of the routes give a result which is a multiple of 5? Try to explain why.

✤ If four people were to choose different routes through the maze:
- what is the lowest possible total of all four?
- what is the highest?
- how many different totals **can you get** for four people?

✤ Design a maze so that all the routes give results which are multiples of 4.

Start →	52 →	15 →	35
↓	↓	↓	↓
27	46	12	45
↓	↓	↓	↓
29	18	35	18
↓	↓	↓	↓
78 →	21 →	15 →	Finish

Name ____________________

Pony jumps

A game for two players.

You will need: a counter each and a calculator.

✣ Choose a course and put your counter by the first number. Then enter that number on to your calculator display.

✣ Take it in turns to change each number to the next using your calculator. If you make a mistake, miss a turn. You must not use the cancel/clear key. Write all your calculations on the logs.

✣ The winner is the player who gets to the rosette first.

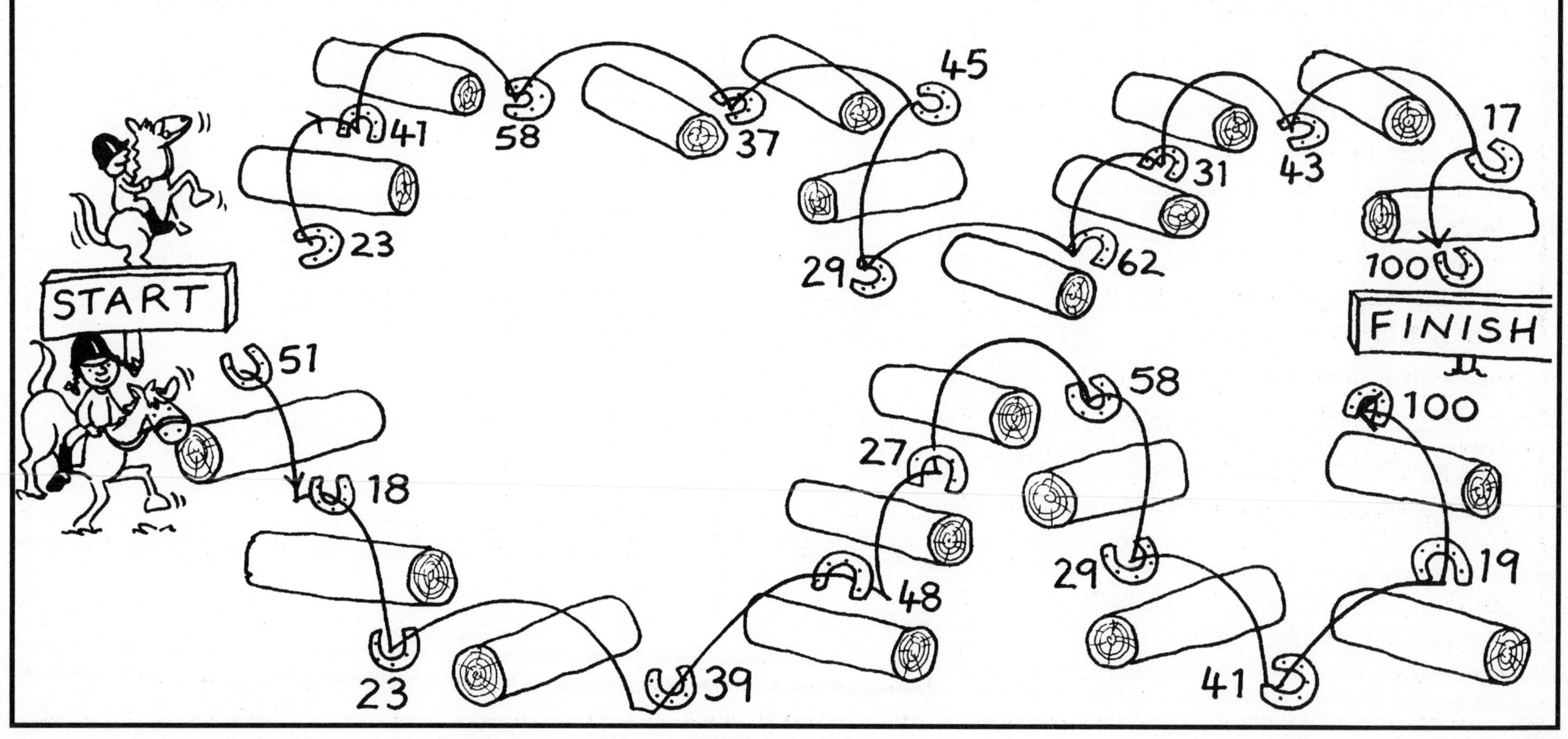

Name ____________________

Mystery keystrokes

For each of these sets of mappings (or changes) a calculator was set up in advance so that the second number could be displayed by entering the first number and pressing [=].

✤ What keystrokes were used to set up the calculator each time? Record the keystrokes below each set of mappings.

3 → 9 4 → 12 7 → 21	6 → 16 4 → 14 9 → 19	11 → 8 16 → 13 21 → 18	3 → 1 9 → 3 15 → 5	3 → 30 4 → 40 7 → 70
6 → 8.1 7 → 9.1 8 → 10.1	15 → 3 60 → 12 75 → 15	4 → 2.5 5 → 3.5 6.5 → 5	33 → 3 88 → 8 121 → 11	3 → 0.3 4 → 0.4 70 → 7

You can change 5 → 20 by setting up the calculator to add 15, or to multiply by 4, or to divide by 0.25, or to subtract –15.

✤ Try to find at least two different ways of setting up the calculator to do each of these mappings:

3 → 30	4 → 12	5 → 100	20 → 4	65 → 13
0.4 → 0.2	0.5 → 0.1	100 → 10	42 → 2.1	500 → 600

Name ____________________

English sovereigns

- Use your calculator to find out who were the three oldest reigning sovereigns.
- Who reigned for more than ten years?
- Who reigned for between five and eight years?

	Born	Died	Reign began	Reign ended
William I	1027	1087	1066	1087
William II	1056	1100	1087	1100
Henry I	1068	1135	1100	1135
Stephen	1097?	1154	1135	1154
Matilda	1102	1167	1141	1141
Henry II	1133	1189	1154	1189
Richard I	1157	1199	1189	1199
John	1167?	1216	1199	1216
Henry III	1207	1272	1216	1272
Edward I	1239	1307	1272	1307
Edward II	1284	1327	1307	1327
Edward III	1312	1377	1327	1377
Richard II	1367	1400	1377	1399
Henry IV	1367	1413	1399	1413
Henry V	1387	1422	1413	1422
Henry VI	1421	1471	1422 1470	1461 1471
Edward IV	1442	1483	1461 1471	1470 1483
Edward V	1470	1483?	1483	1483
Richard III	1452	1485	1483	1485

	Born	Died	Reign began	Reign ended
Henry VII	1457	1509	1485	1509
Henry VIII	1491	1547	1509	1547
Edward VI	1537	1553	1547	1553
Jane Grey	1537	1554	1553	1553
Mary I	1516	1558	1553	1558
Elizabeth I	1533	1603	1558	1603
James I	1566	1625	1603	1625
Charles I	1600	1649	1625	1649
Charles II	1630	1685	1660	1685
James II	1633	1701	1685	1688
William III	1650	1702	1689	1702
Mary II	1662	1694	1689	1694
Anne	1665	1714	1702	1714
George I	1660	1727	1714	1727
George II	1683	1760	1727	1760
George III	1738	1820	1760	1820
George IV	1762	1830	1820	1830
William IV	1765	1837	1830	1837
Victoria	1819	1901	1837	1901
Edward VII	1841	1910	1901	1910
George V	1865	1936	1910	1936
Edward VIII	1894	1972	1936	1936
George VI	1895	1952	1936	1952
Elizabeth II	1926		1952	

Name ____________________

Product pairs

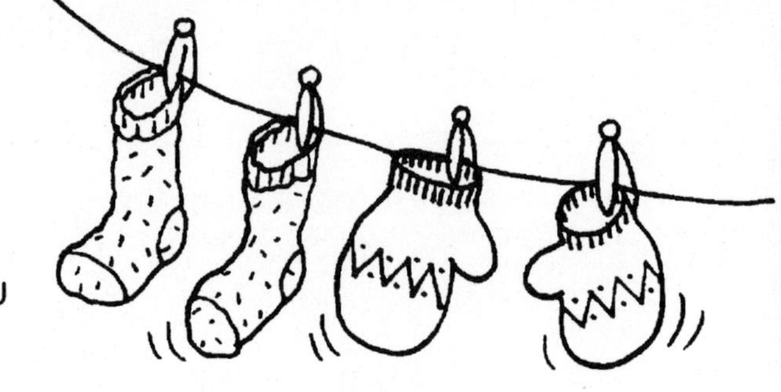

✤ Cut out these cards and use your calculator to help you to match those calculations which have the same products. What clues can you use?

✤ Now sort the cards according to the last digit of the answer. What do you notice? Do you need to work out the products?

✤ Sort the cards according to whether the answers are less than 100, between 100 and 500, or more than 500.

27 × 17	3 × 12	22 × 12	2 × 32
8 × 2	5 × 125	43 × 243	8 × 12
129 × 81	4 × 16	6 × 24	4 × 4
25 × 25	51 × 9	2 × 48	12 × 12
11 × 24	63 × 13	15 × 13	39 × 21
81 × 15	27 × 45	9 × 4	5 × 39

Name ____________________

Exploring multiplication

You will need: the multiplication grid, paper, a pencil and a calculator.

✤ Find all those numbers on the grid which end in a 4. Write down the multiplication questions which give those numbers. For example: 3 × 8 = 24

✤ Use your calculator to help you to make up some more questions where the answer ends in a 4.

✤ Do the same for numbers which end in a 1.

✤ Find these missing numbers. Use your multiplication grid to help you.

3 × □ = 51	11 × □ = 231	9 × □ = 171	7 × □ = 91
4 × □ = 56	□ × 6 = 96	12 × □ = 108	□ × 3 = 36
6 × □ = 42	21 × □ = 189	□ × 12 = 72	7 × □ = 112

✤ Find these missing numbers. Use your calculator to help you.

13 × □ = 1261	121 × □ = 13431	29 × □ = 2871
24 × □ = 2016	□ × 56 = 39536	212 × □ = 66356
56 × □ = 6272	21 × □ = 8484	□ × 612 = 609552
57 × □ = 1311	□ × 113 = 5876	117 × □ = 7722

The soroban: 1

The soroban, or Japanese abacus, uses two spaces representing heaven and earth. Counters 'in heaven' are worth five times as much as those 'on earth'.

This soroban shows nought.

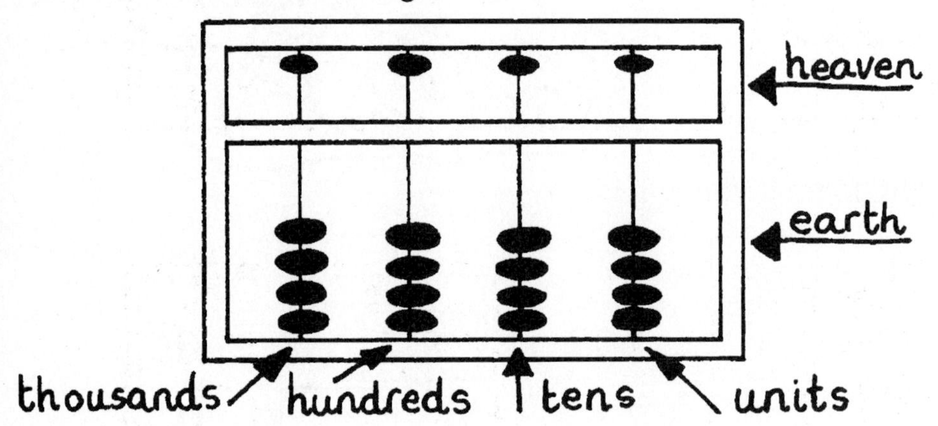

You move the counters on to the central bar to show a number.

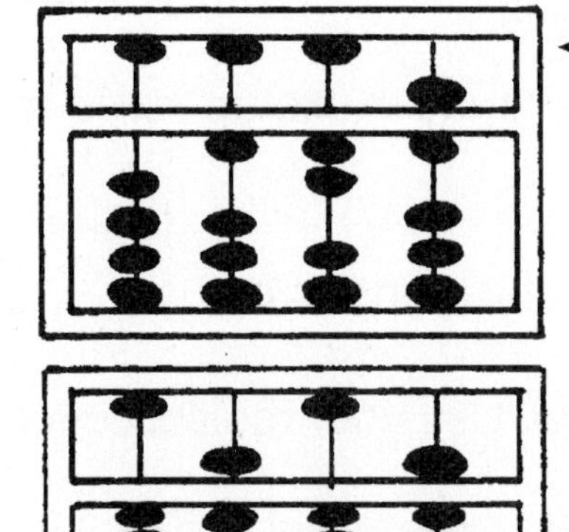

For example: one hundred has been moved. Two tens have been moved. One five and one unit have been moved. The number on this soroban is:
100 + 20 + 5 + 1 = 126

And on this soroban, the number is:
2 000 + 500 + 100 + 30 + 5 + 2 = 2 637

✤ Use your calculator to match each number to the correct soroban. Draw lines from the numbers to the sorobans.

3 355 | 7 807 | 

| 5 784 | 5 082

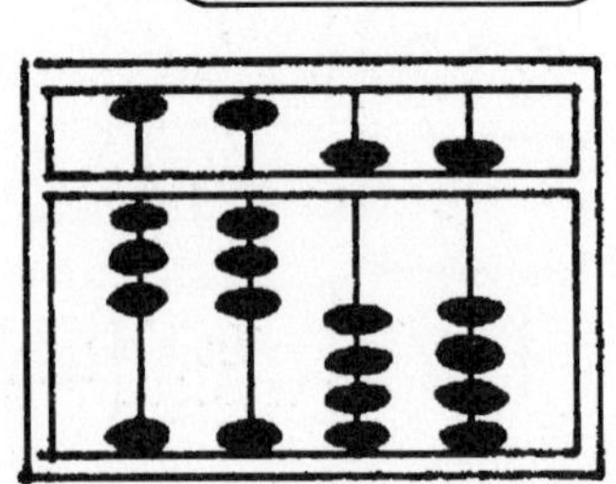
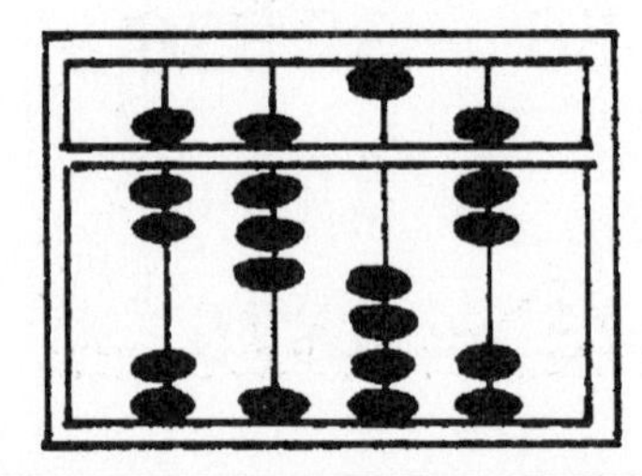
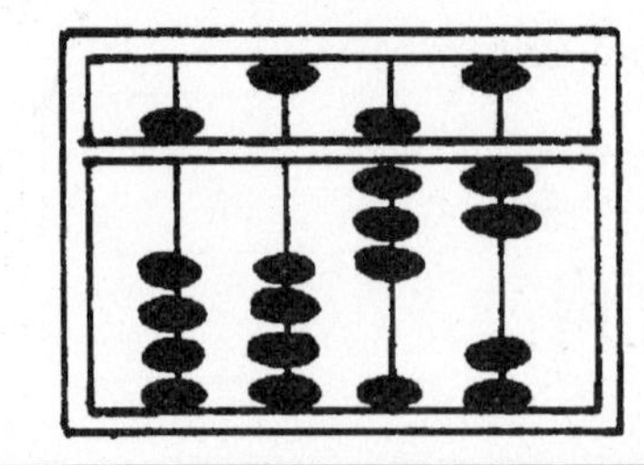
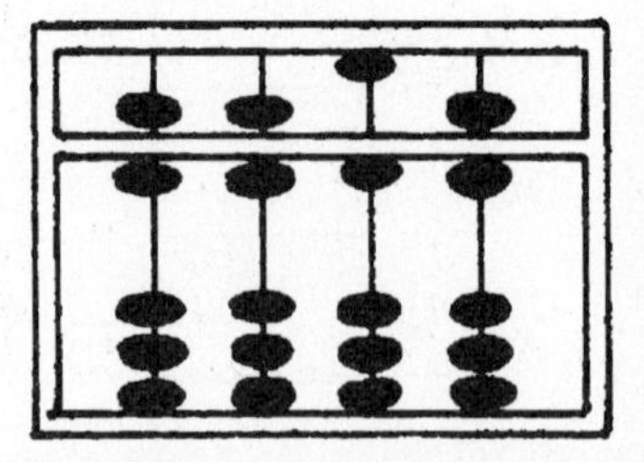

Name ____________________

The soroban: 2

✤ Part of each of these sorobans has been hidden. Use your calculator to help you to work out what numbers they could be showing.

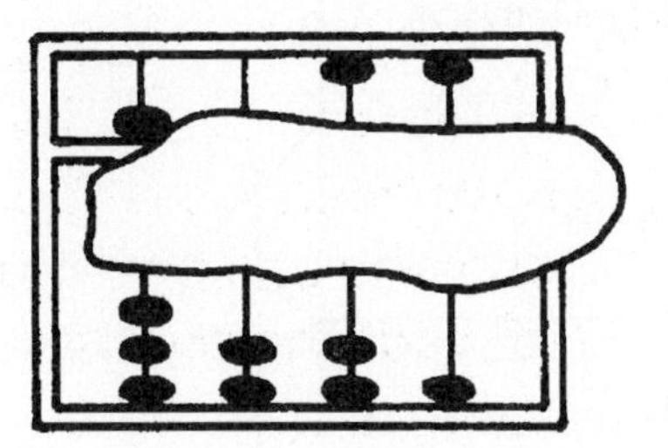

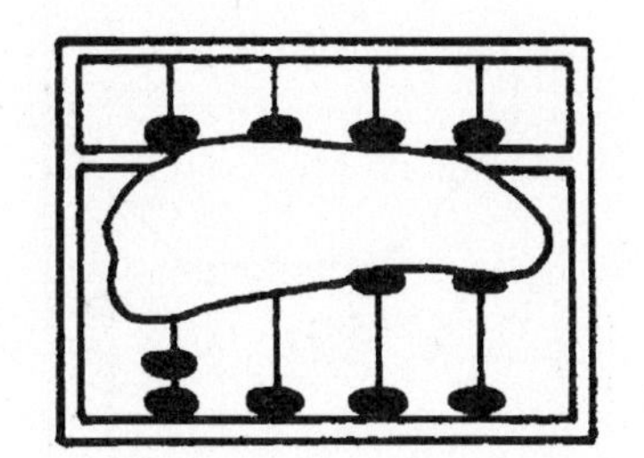

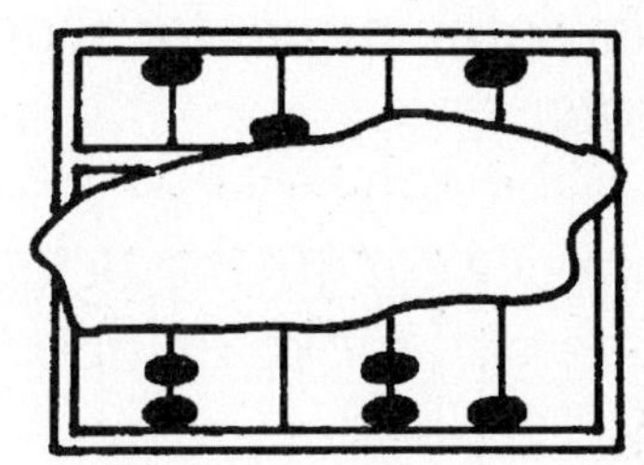

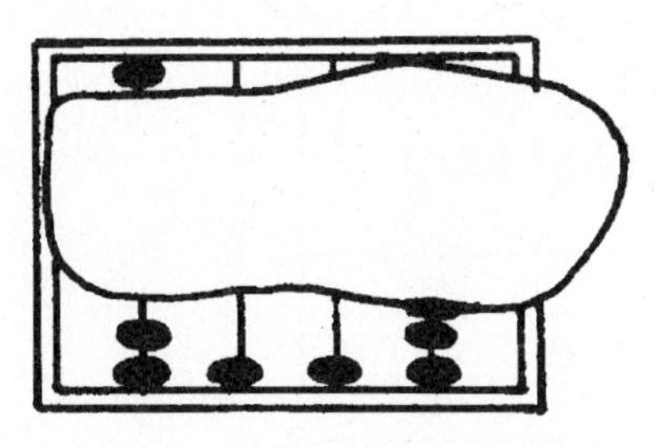

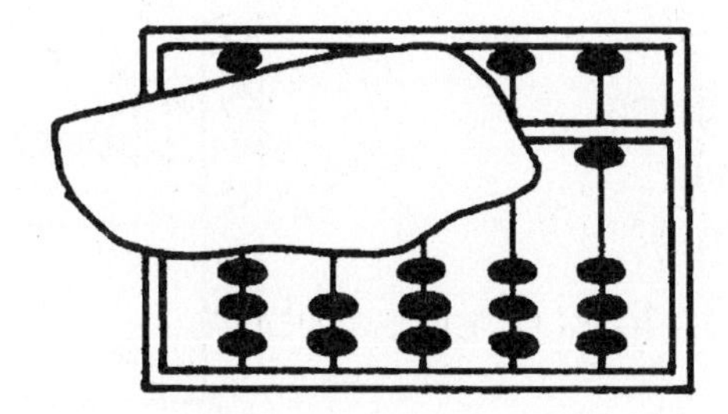

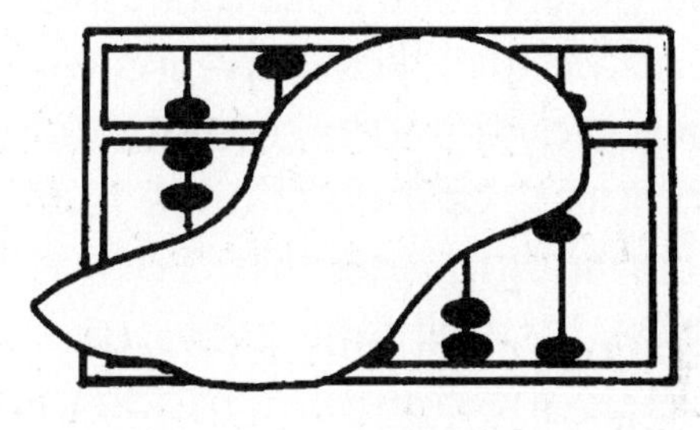

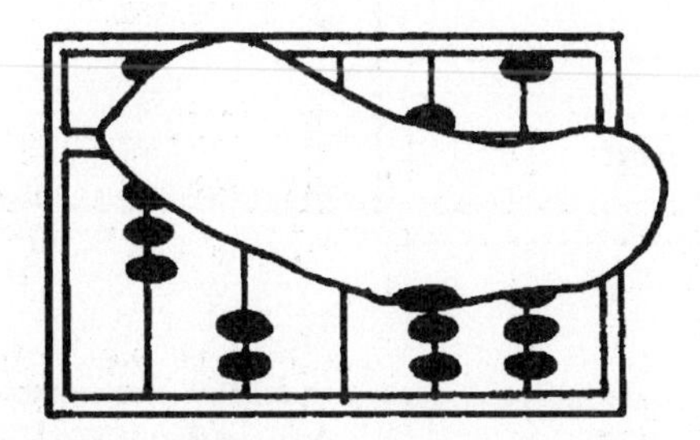

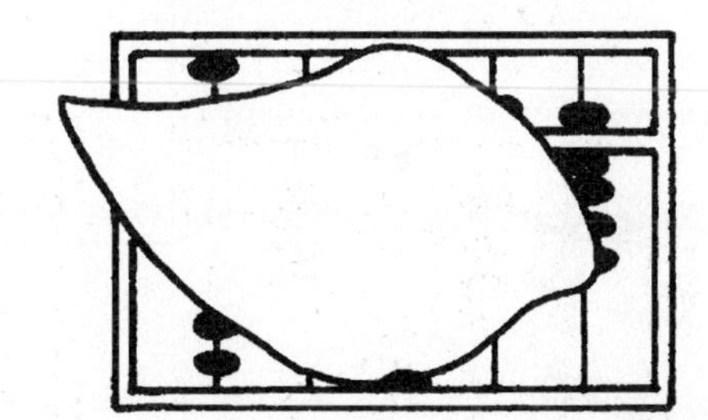

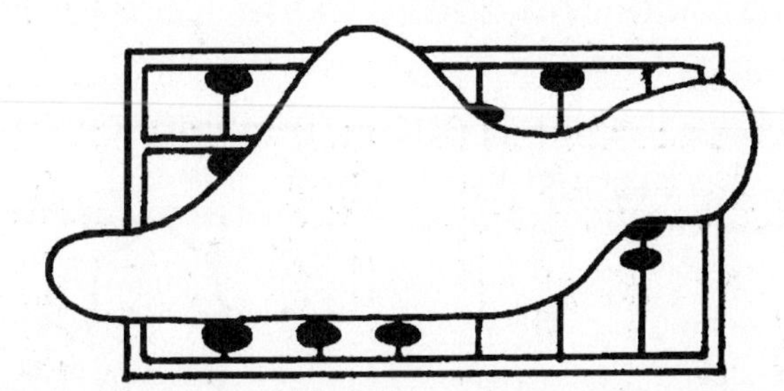

Rolling operations

A game for two or more players.

You will need: scissors, adhesive, two dice, pencils, some paper for score sheets and a calculator.

✤ Carefully cut out the octagonal prism net opposite and make an operations roller.

✤ Choose who will go first and then take turns. At each turn, the player begins with 0.
✤ The player rolls both dice and the operations roller and then follows the instructions on the roller.
✤ Each player's turn continues until the roller gives 'End of turn!', or they choose to stop. If the player risks continuing and rolls 'Back to 0. End of turn!', then they lose all their previous scores.
✤ Add up the numbers made in that turn.
✤ The total score for each turn is recorded on the score sheet and added to the score for the previous turn.
✤ Have five turns each. The winner is the player with the highest total score.

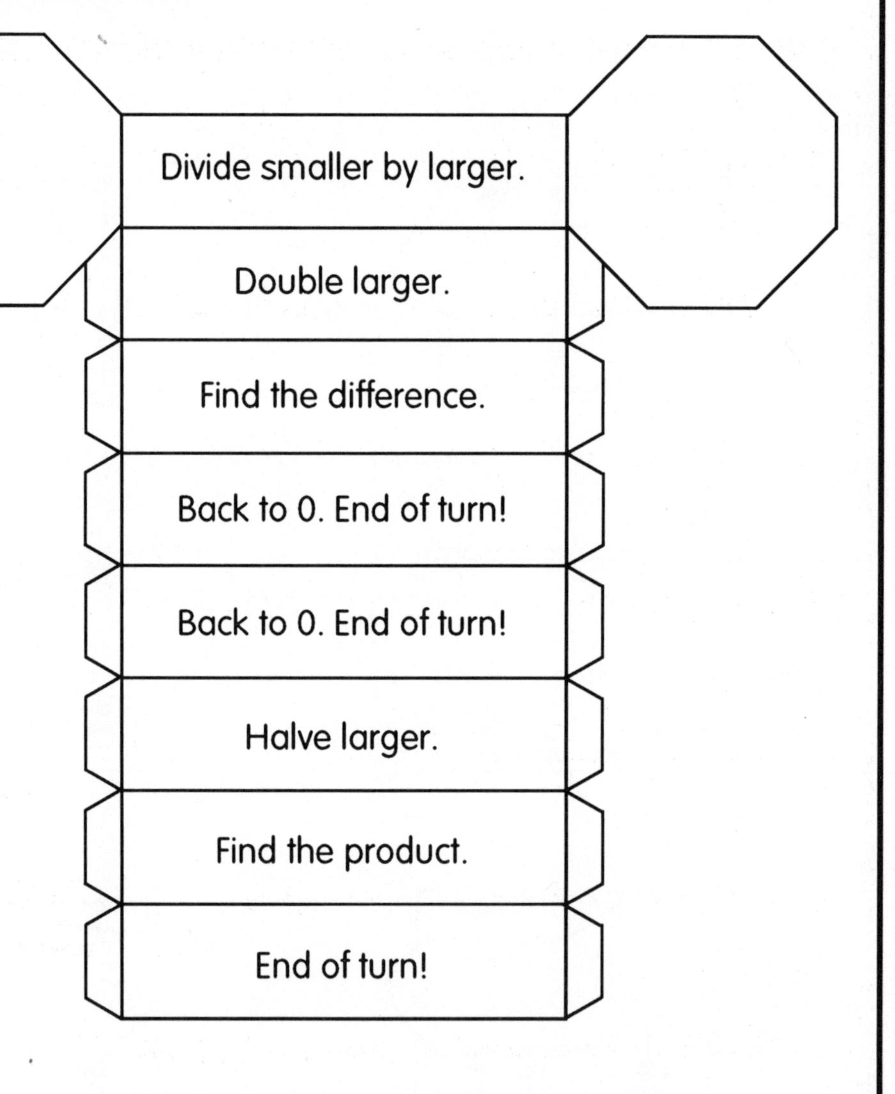

Name ____________________

Check those prices

You will need: the price label cards and a calculator.

- ✤ Use your calculator to add up the prices on all the cards.
- ✤ Add up all the prices on the even numbered cards.
- ✤ Add up all the prices on the odd numbered cards.
- ✤ The prices on which two cards total £3.14?
- ✤ The prices on which two cards total £6.45?
- ✤ The prices on which two cards total £1.58?
- ✤ The prices on which two cards total £3.44?

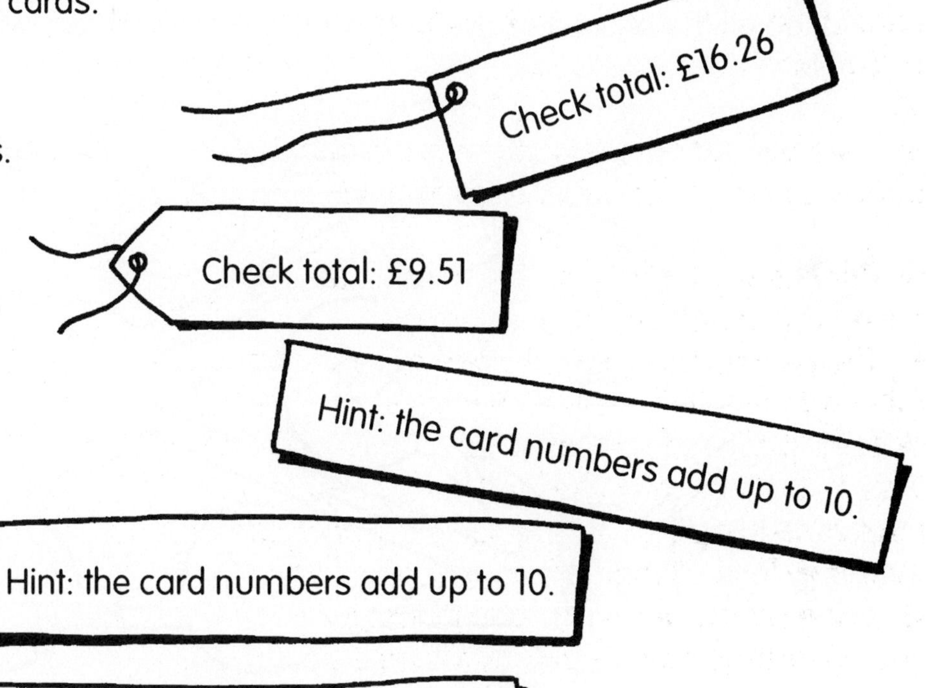

Amazing products

- Choose a route through this maze and follow it from the start to the finish. Use your calculator to find the different products.
- Try some other routes. Are any of your answers the same? Try to explain why.
- What do all the answers have in common? Try to explain why.

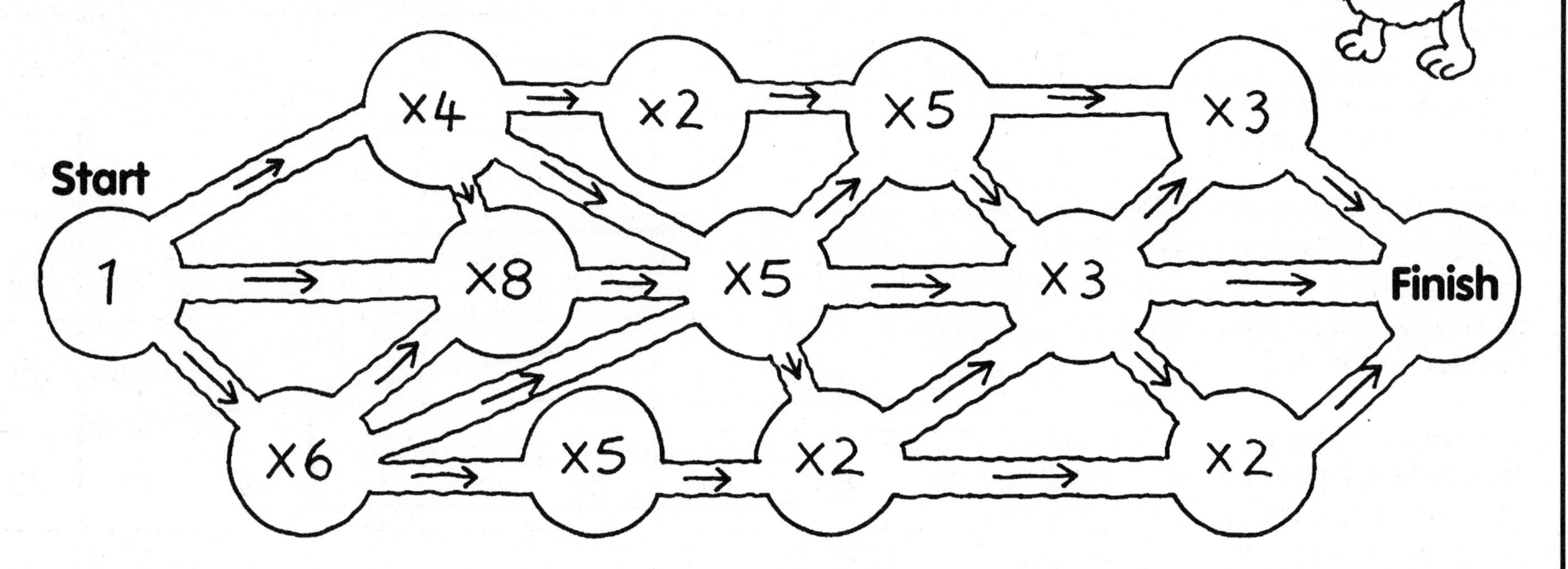

- Try starting with the number 10. What happens to your answers at the finish?
- Try starting with 100, 1000 and 10 000. Try to explain the different results.
- Will the answers be whole numbers if you start with the number 0.1 or 0.01? Try to explain why.

Name ____________

One for primes

A game for two or more players.

You will need: a counter and a calculator for each player, and one dice.

✤ Decide who will go first and then take turns to throw the dice.

✤ Move to the **first** number on the board **which is exactly divisible by the number on the dice**.

✤ As all numbers are divisible by 1, if you throw a 1, you can only move to the next shaded square, a **prime number**. (Prime numbers are only divisible by 1 and themselves.)

✤ You must finish on 100, by throwing a 2 or a 5.

Start	2	3	4	5	6	7	8	9	10
11	12	13	14	15	16	17	18	19	20
21	22	23	24	25	26	27	28	29	30
31	32	33	34	35	36	37	38	39	40
41	42	43	44	45	46	47	48	49	50
51	52	53	54	55	56	57	58	59	60
61	62	63	64	65	66	67	68	69	70
71	72	73	74	75	76	77	78	79	80
81	82	83	84	85	86	87	88	89	90
91	92	93	94	95	96	97	98	99	100

Place value check

- In each cloud, ring the numbers that obey the rule.
- Use your calculator to add together the ringed numbers in each cloud. Check the result with the check total.
- Design your own set of place value clouds and test them on a friend.

Rule: 3 in the **tens** column.
345 673 832
31 33 40302
436 50336
42032
Check total: 93700

Rule: 5 in the **units** column.
505 52 9032
1275 125
25 6715
4655
Check total: 13300

Rule: 0 in the **tens** column.
1034 203 6802
1800345
59007 9078
Check total: 66012

Rule: 1 in the **thousands** column.
1657 4123 78123
9012 81006
21789 11890
Check total: 116342

Rule: 7 in the **hundreds** column.
7978 27 6770
97345 1789
7458 74 176 768
Check total: 9327

Name ____________________

Pentomino puzzle

Pentominoes are shapes made from five squares which join along their edges, not at their corners. Two are shaded for you in the rectangle below. There are ten more pentominoes hidden in the rectangle. They are all different. The other ten pentominoes each have five squares whose total is 50.

✤ Use your calculator to help you to find the ten missing pentominoes. Shade each one in a different colour.

3	8	9	14	17	8	8	9	14	11
16	3	5	7	16	3			15	15
3	16	7	16	7	5	3		7	3
	13	15	11	11	16			10	4
	10	8	8	13	13	16	9	16	10
			16	8	17	3	6	8	11

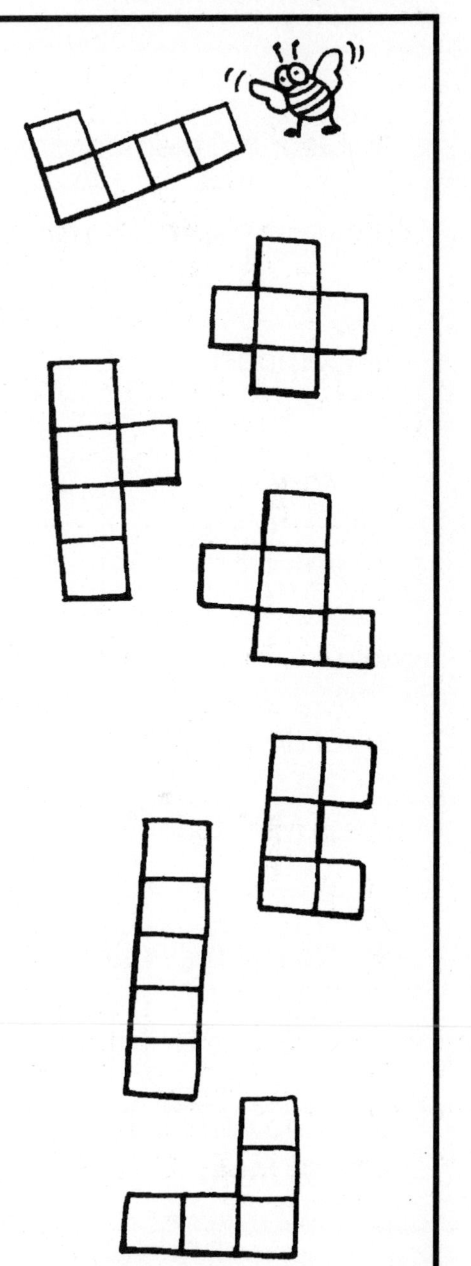

Name ____________

Memory search

✤ Clear the memory on your calculator by

pressing: MRC MRC C

or (perhaps): MC C

✤ Make this sequence of keystrokes:

22 M+ 12 M+

What is shown on the calculator display?

What do you think is in the memory?

Press MRC to find out.

✤ Do not press clear. Continue with:

14 M+ 32 M+

What do you think is in the memory now?
Do not look.

✤ Choose your own number, enter it and

then press: M+

✤ Continue adding until you think you have exactly 100 in the memory.

Press MRC to see if you are right.

✤ Try this several times with different sets of numbers. Can you get exactly 100?

✤ Can you find a set of five numbers which add up to 100 where you only use any digit once?

Using the +/– key

✤ Cut out these cards and use your calculator to help you to match those which have the same answer.

✤ Match those questions which have the same digits in. Why do you think that they give different answers?

6 [+] 4 [+/–] [=]	8 [–] 3 [+/–] [=]	1 [+] 1 [+/–] [=]	8 [+] 2 [+/–] [=]
6 [+] 5 [+/–] [=]	6 [–] 3 [+/–] [=]	7 [–] 3 [+/–] [=]	6 [–] 5 [+/–] [=]
1 [–] 1 [+/–] [=]	2 [+] 1 [+/–] [=]	5 [–] 5 [+/–] [=]	5 [+] 4 [+/–] [=]
6 [–] 4 [+/–] [=]	8 [–] 2 [+/–] [=]	8 [+] 3 [+/–] [=]	5 [+] 5 [+/–] [=]
5 [–] 1 [+/–] [=]	5 [+] 1 [+/–] [=]	3 [+] 2 [+/–] [=]	7 [+] 3 [+/–] [=]
5 [–] 4 [+/–] [=]	3 [–] 2 [+/–] [=]	2 [–] 1 [+/–] [=]	6 [+] 3 [+/–] [=]

Name ____________________

Take a stride

The pictures opposite show the tracks of a harvest mouse, a hedgehog and a water vole.

✤ Measure the stride of each animal.

✤ Use your calculator to find out how many strides each animal would take to cover:

- 1 metre;
- 20 metres;
- 100 metres;
- 1 kilometre.

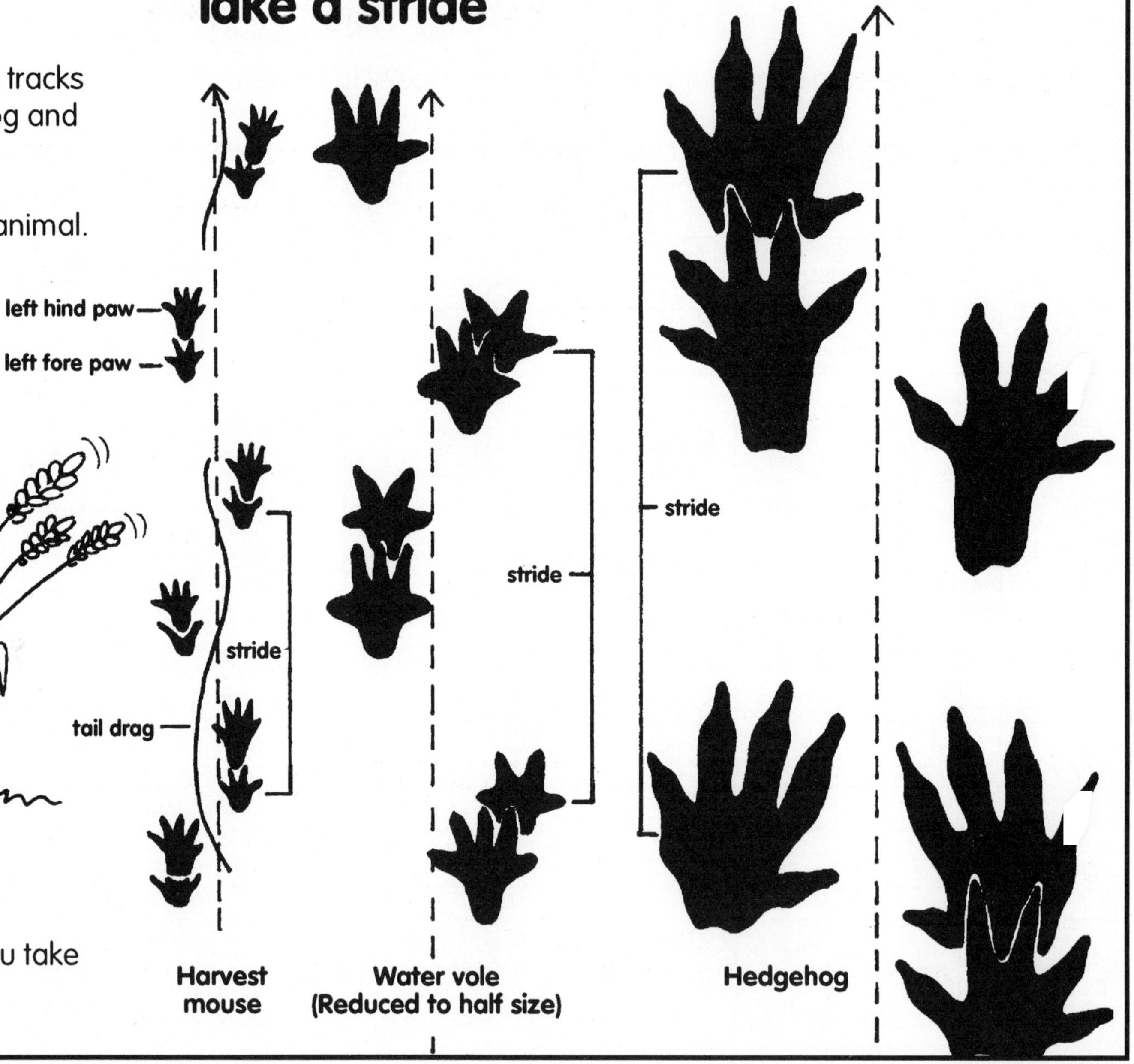

✤ Measure your own stride.

✤ How many strides would you take to cover 1 kilometre?

left hind paw
left fore paw
stride
tail drag
Harvest mouse
stride
Water vole (Reduced to half size)
stride
Hedgehog

Name ____________________

Lots of rectangles

- Measure the lengths and widths of these rectangles.
- Use your calculator to find the perimeter and area of each rectangle.

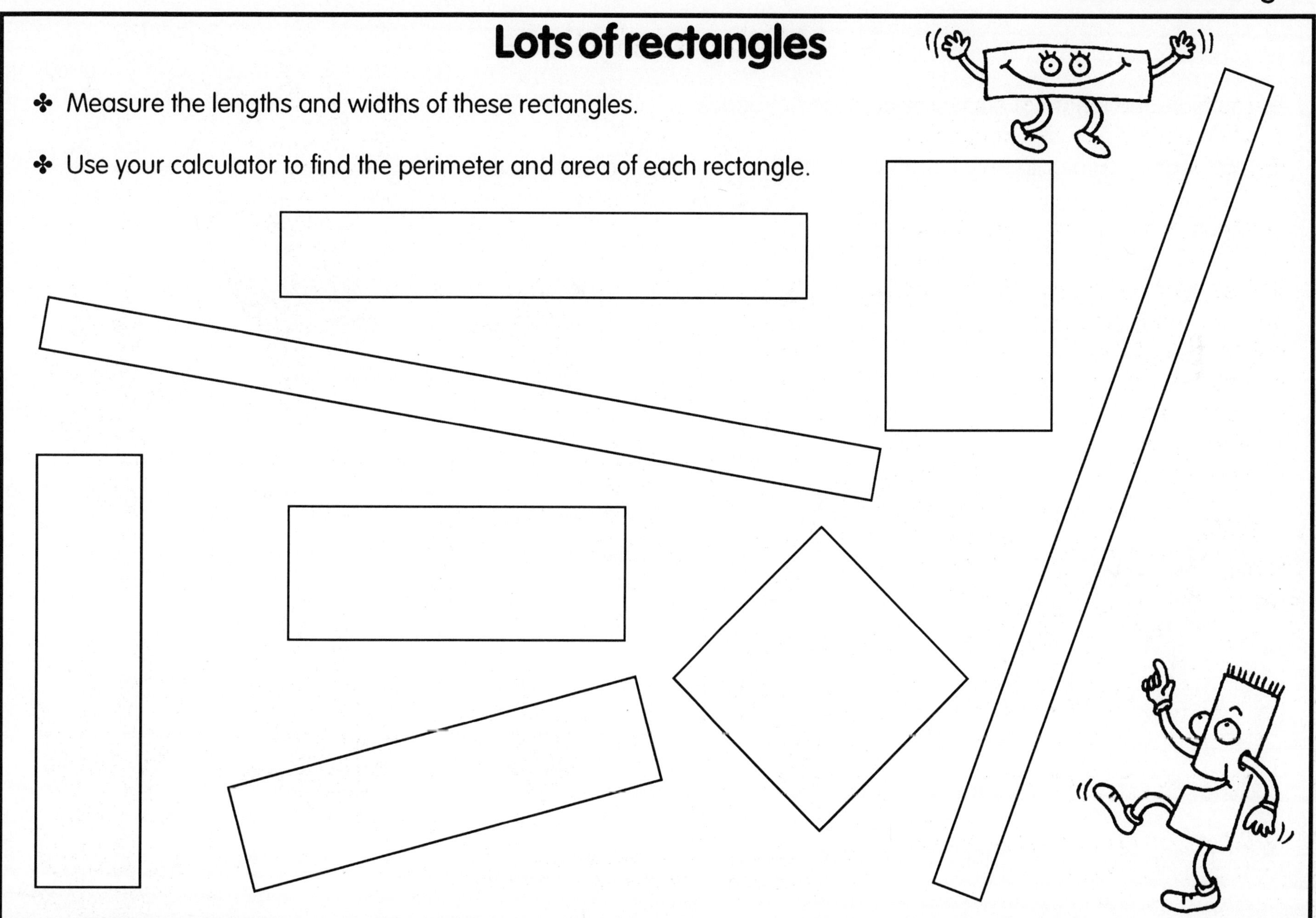

Name ____________________

Hexagons galore

✤ Measure the length of each side of these hexagons.

✤ Use your calculator to help you to work out the perimeter of each hexagon.

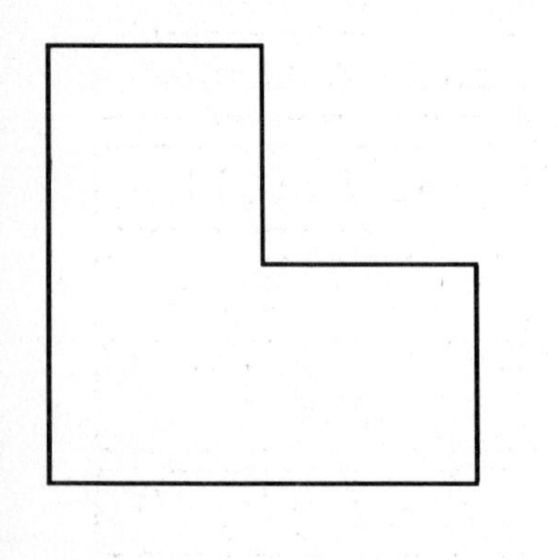
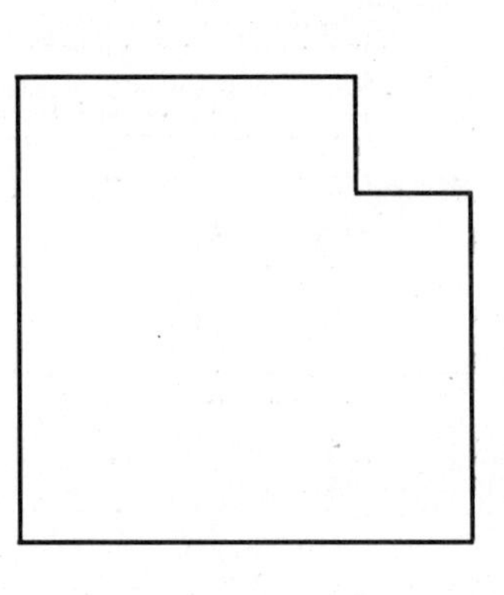
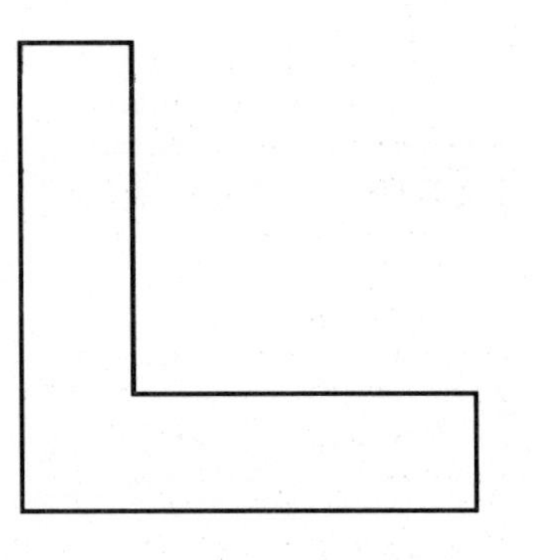
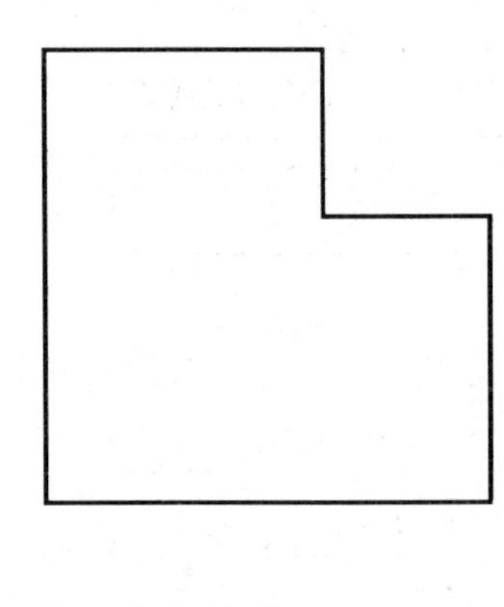
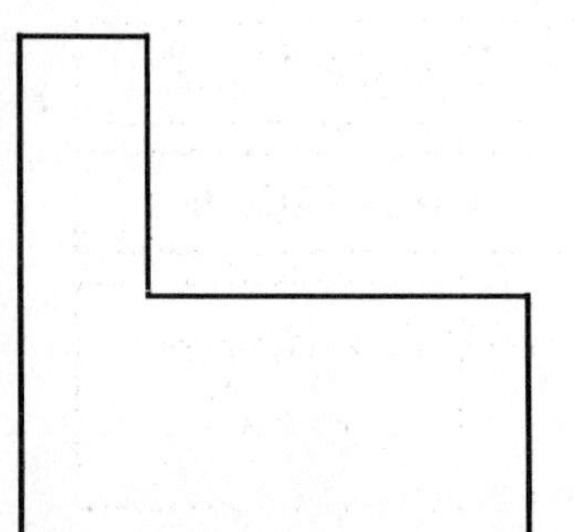
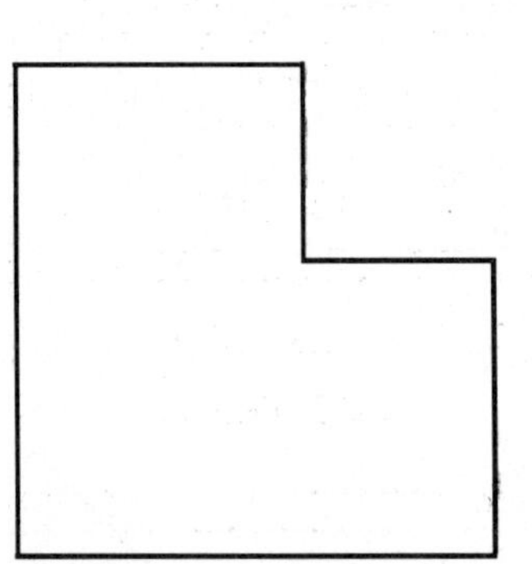
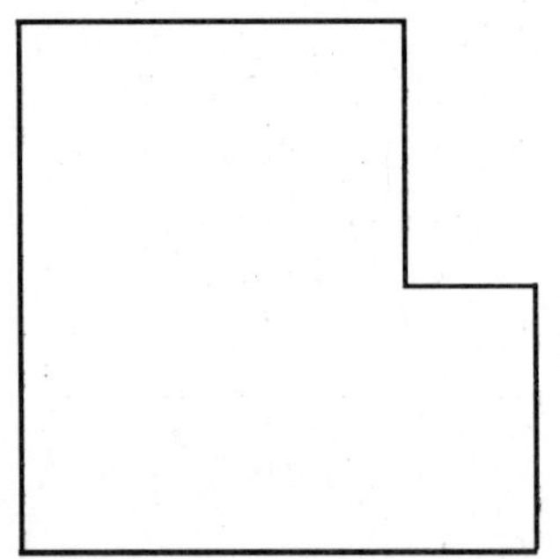
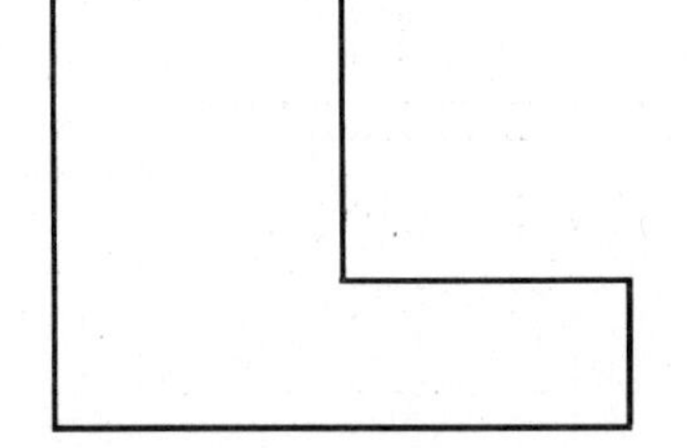

✤ What do these shapes have in common?

✤ Draw some more hexagons which have the same property as these hexagons.

Name ____________________

There and back again

✤ Work through each of these flow charts lots of times using your calculator. What do you notice?

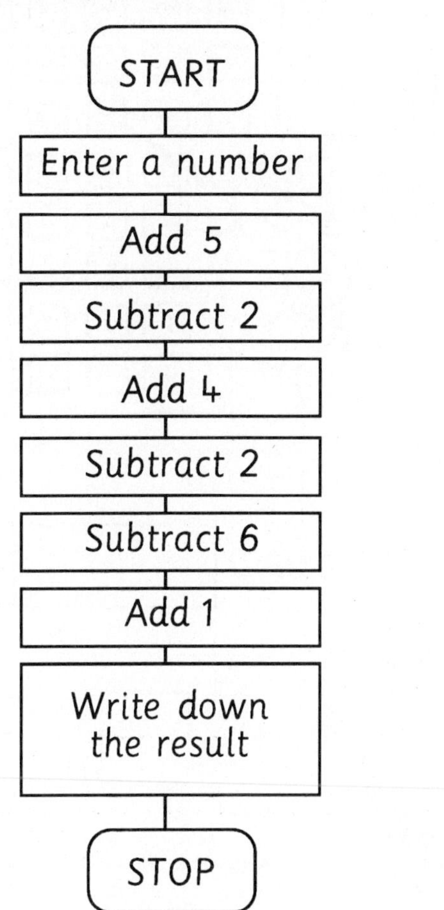

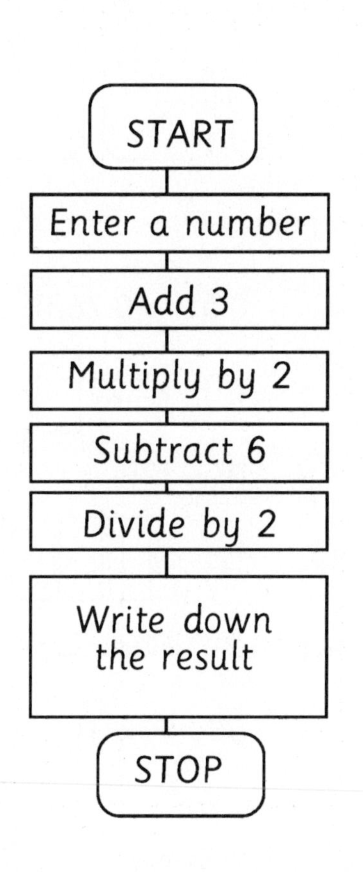

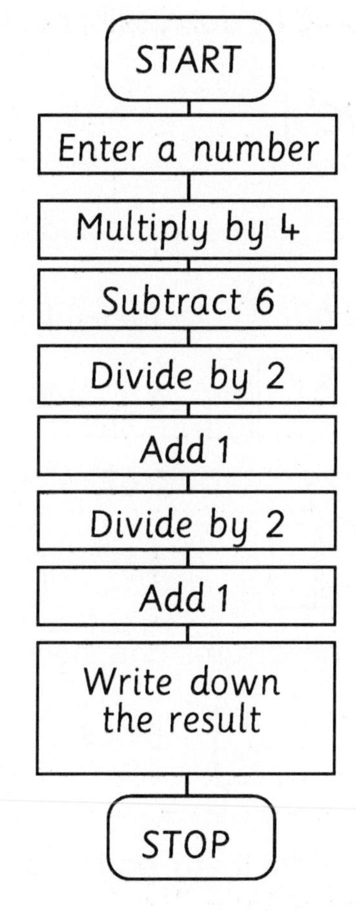

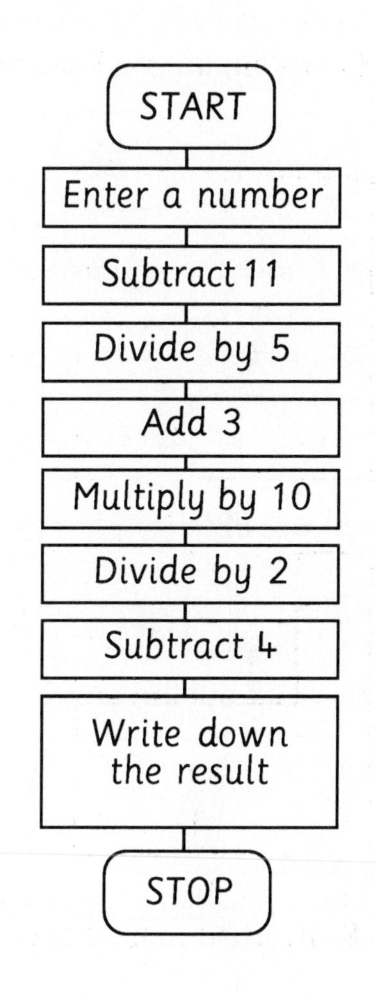

✤ Design your own flow charts which have the same effect.

Name ____________________

Squares of numbers

Some calculators have a special button for squaring numbers (that is, multiplying them by themselves, for example $3^2 = 3 \times 3$), but you can also square using the constant. For example: you can square 12 by doing either of these:

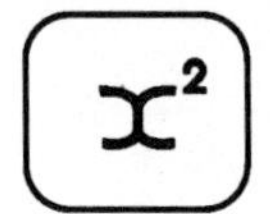

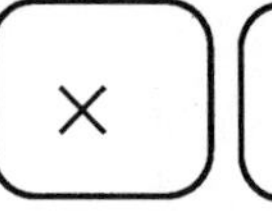

✤ Check the squares of these numbers and find the missing digits:

$33 \rightarrow 1\,089$ $51 \rightarrow 2\,601$ $3.3 \rightarrow 10.89$ $0.51 \rightarrow 0.2601$

$22 \rightarrow$ □□ 4 $32 \rightarrow 1\,0$ □□ $6.4 \rightarrow 40.$□□ $1.11 \rightarrow 1.23$□□

$45^2 = 2\,025$ $27^2 = 729$ $3.67^2 = 13.4689$ $11^2 = 121$ $0.1^2 = 0.01$

$75^2 =$ □□ 25 $17^2 =$ □□ 9 $4.67^2 =$ □1.□089 $121^2 =$ □□□□1 $0.01^2 =$ □

✤ Work out the answers to these sums and then extend the pattern. What do you notice?

$3^2 - 2^2 = 5$ $4^2 - 3^2 =$ □ $5^2 - 4^2 =$ □ $6^2 - 5^2 = 11$ $7^2 - 6^2 =$ □

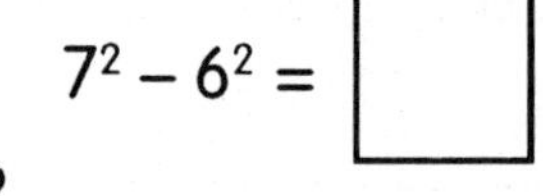

Some numbers, when you square them, end in the same digit, like these:

$25^2 = 625$ $6^2 = 36$

✤ Try to find some more.

Name ____________________

Product squares

- Cut out the nine squares opposite.
- Use your calculator to work out the product of each pair of numbers. Do not write the answers on the cards.
- Put the nine squares together again, to make a large square, so that sides which touch have the same answers.
- Check each position by using your calculator.
- How many different ways can you do this?
- What clues do you use to help you to decide which squares fit where?

9 × 42
64 × 12
18 × 21
54 × 7

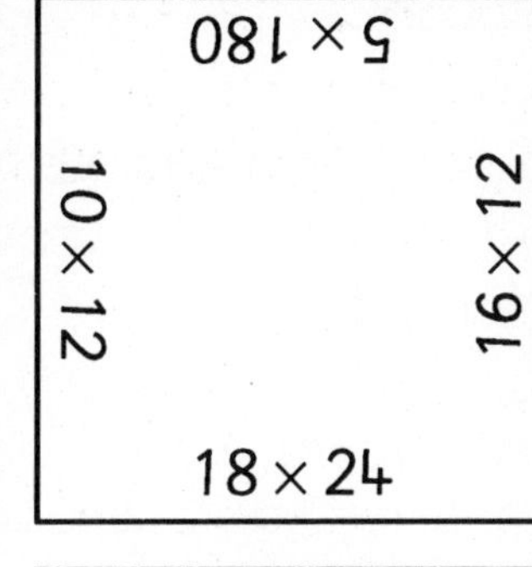

16 × 48
6 × 63
3 × 126
12 × 75

4 × 30
7 × 54
100 × 9
32 × 6

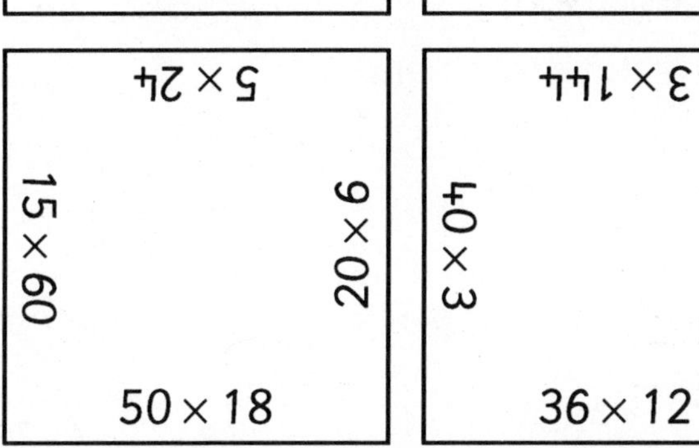

18 × 21
4 × 48
25 × 36
128 × 6

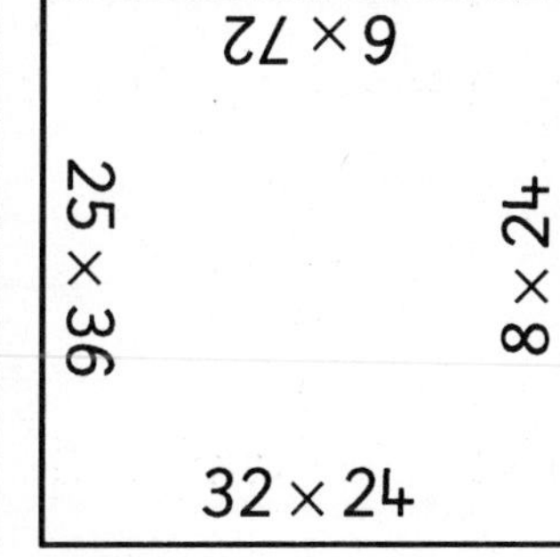

3 × 64
9 × 42
24 × 5
9 × 48

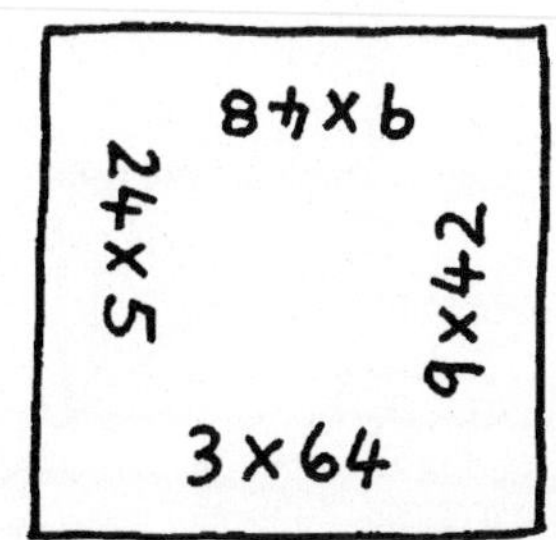

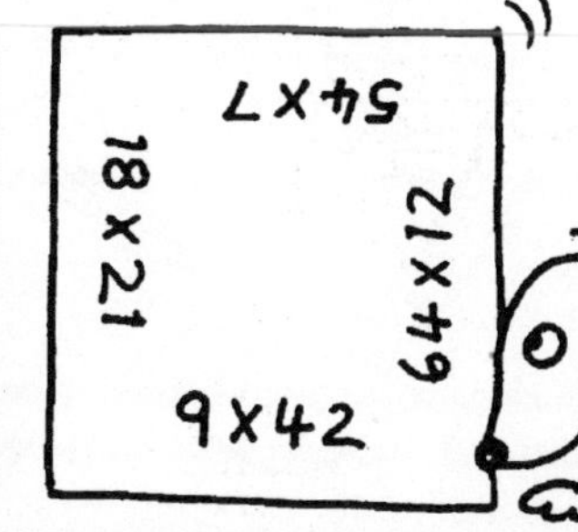

Decimal digit spins

A game for two or more players.

You will need: the three digit spinners, some number cards (for example 2, 3, 4, 6, 8 and 10), and a pencil, score card and calculator for each player.

✤ Deal each player a number card.

✤ Spin the three spinners.

✤ Using the three spinner digits, each player must make up a decimal number as close to their card number as possible.

✤ Each player's score is the difference between the number they make and their number card. Use your calculator to work this out.

✤ Play ten rounds. The player with the lowest total score is the winner.

Name ____________________

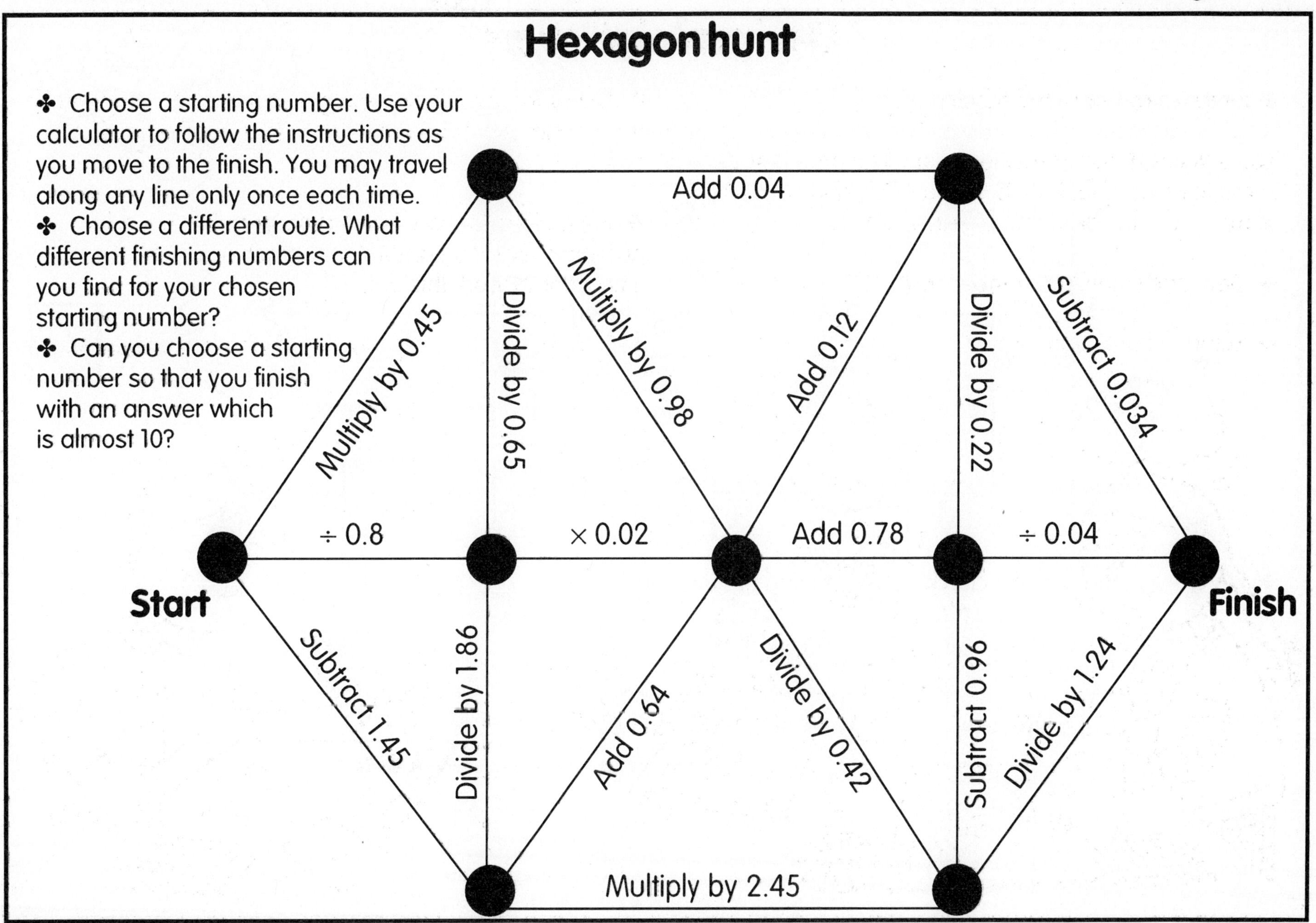
Hexagon hunt
✤ Choose a starting number. Use your calculator to follow the instructions as you move to the finish. You may travel along any line only once each time.
✤ Choose a different route. What different finishing numbers can you find for your chosen starting number?
✤ Can you choose a starting number so that you finish with an answer which is almost 10?
Start
Finish
Add 0.04
Multiply by 0.45
Divide by 0.65
Multiply by 0.98
Add 0.12
Divide by 0.22
Subtract 0.034
÷ 0.8
× 0.02
Add 0.78
÷ 0.04
Subtract 1.45
Divide by 1.86
Add 0.64
Divide by 0.42
Subtract 0.96
Divide by 1.24
Multiply by 2.45

Name ______________________

Percentage keys

✤ First find out about your calculator.
Which sequences of key presses give you the correct answer?

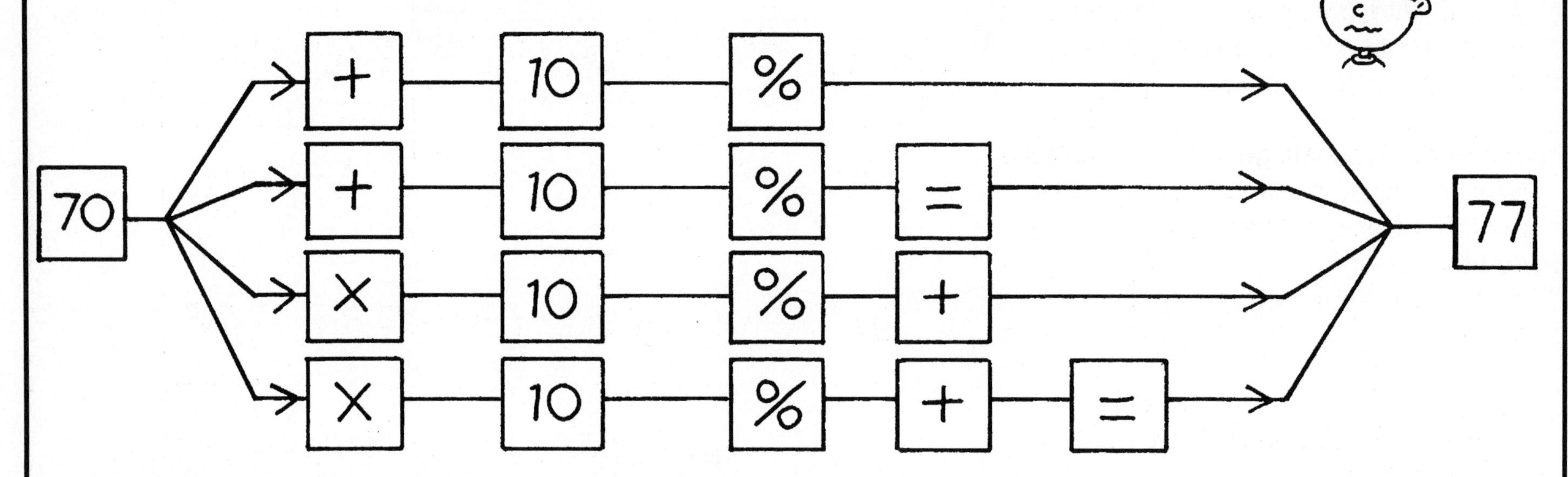

✤ Here are some more to check or to try to find the missing numbers.

400 → 440   50 → 55   500 → 550   10 → 11   101 → 111.1   707 → 777.7

200 → ☐   300 → ☐   75 → ☐   250 → ☐   25 → ☐

☐ → 66   ☐ → 253   ☐ → 55.55   ☐ → 666.6   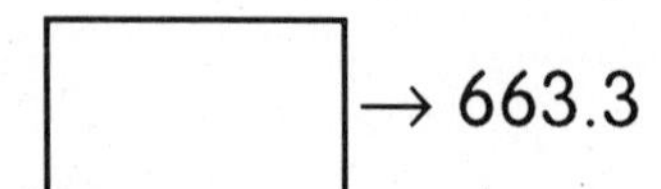 → 663.3

Name ____________________

Percentage four-in-a-row: 1

A game for two players.

You will need: a set of counters, each in a different colour, for each player and a calculator.

- Choose who will go first and then take turns to choose a number, enter it on to the calculator and add 10%.
- If the result matches a number on the board, claim that square with a counter.
- The winner is the first player with four counters in a row; horizontally, vertically or diagonally.
- Play the game several times.
- How do you know which numbers to choose?

792	198	704	924	176	132
264	33	506	143	66	814
88	396	220	638	286	308
11	330	484	22	154	572
242	110	418	55	44	374
550	440	77	352	121	99

Percentage four-in-a-row: 2

A game for two players.

You will need: a set of counters, each in a different colour, for each player and a calculator.

✤ Choose who will go first and then take turns to choose a number, enter it on to the calculator and add 20%.

✤ If the result matches a number on the board, claim that square with a counter.

✤ The winner is the first player with four counters in a row; horizontally, vertically or diagonally.

✤ Play the game several times.

✤ How do you know which numbers to choose?

150	120	210	96	162	270
216	144	294	102	66	360
72	312	138	264	204	108
180	114	60	192	78	300
330	90	48	132	42	156
222	168	240	30	252	174

Name ____________________

Percentage of

35 out of 100 is 35%, 51 out of 100 is 51%, and 98 out of 100 is 98%.
We can also write these calculations as follows:

$\frac{35}{100} = 35\%$ $\frac{51}{100} = 51\%$ $\frac{98}{100} = 98\%$

Those are straightforward, but how do you work out 35 as a percentage of 140?

✤ Which of these sequences of key presses give you the correct answer?

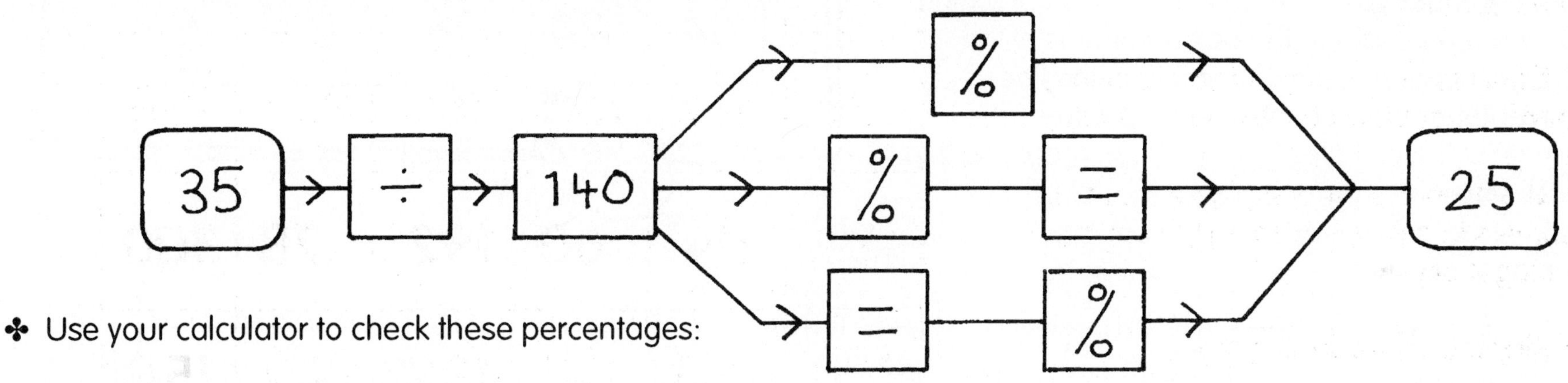

✤ Use your calculator to check these percentages:

$\frac{20}{50} = 40\%$ $\frac{25}{40} = 62.5\%$ $\frac{20}{25} = 80\%$ $\frac{16}{32} = 50\%$ $\frac{18}{24} = 75\%$ $\frac{71}{100} = 71\%$

✤ Now work these out as percentages, but try to guess first:

$\frac{2}{5}$ = ☐ % $\frac{3}{4}$ = ☐ % $\frac{4}{5}$ = ☐ % $\frac{5}{25}$ = ☐ % $\frac{2}{25}$ = ☐ %

$\frac{3}{30}$ = ☐ % $\frac{23}{50}$ = ☐ % $\frac{25}{125}$ = ☐ % $\frac{2}{200}$ = ☐ % $\frac{16}{64}$ = ☐ %

Name ______________________

Percentage three together

A game for two players.

You will need: two different coloured pencils and one calculator.

✤ Choose who will go first and then take turns.

✤ Choose a number from the box opposite and any other number you wish. Use the calculator to find out what percentage the box number is of the chosen number, mark the result on the line. If your percentage is not on the line, miss a turn. The winner is the first player to get three marks next to each other.

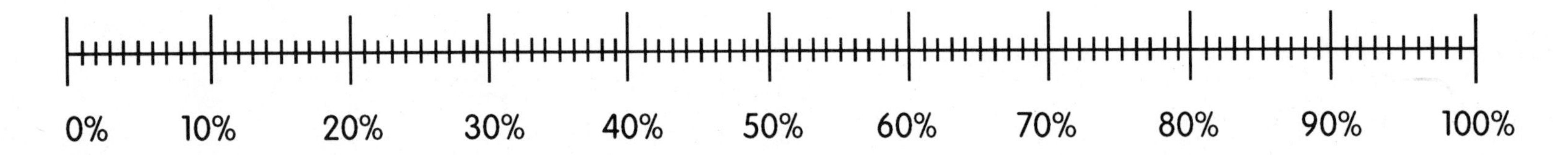

✤ Play the game again, but now you choose both numbers.

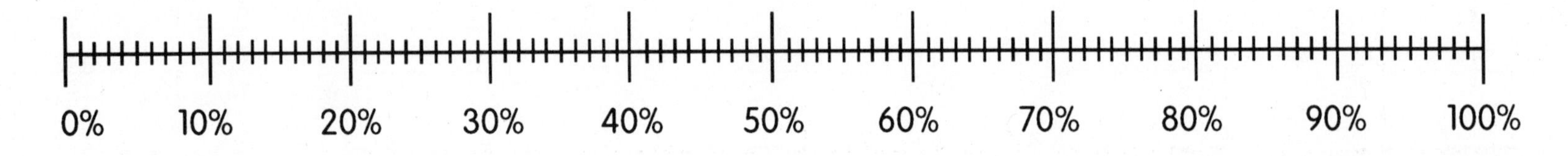

Range attack

A game for two players.

You will need: two different coloured pencils and one calculator.

✤ Decide who will be Player 1 and who will be Player 2 and then take turns.

✤ Player 1 enters 100 on to the calculator and can then multiply or divide by any other number to try to get a result inside Range 1. If they are successful, they mark the position of the result on the line.

✤ Player 2 then multiplies or divides Player 1's result by any other number to try to get inside Range 2.

✤ Any results not in the player's range go into the 'Free zone' and the other player gets two turns.

✤ Player 1 then uses Player 2's result and so on.

✤ The first player with ten numbers marked on their number line wins.

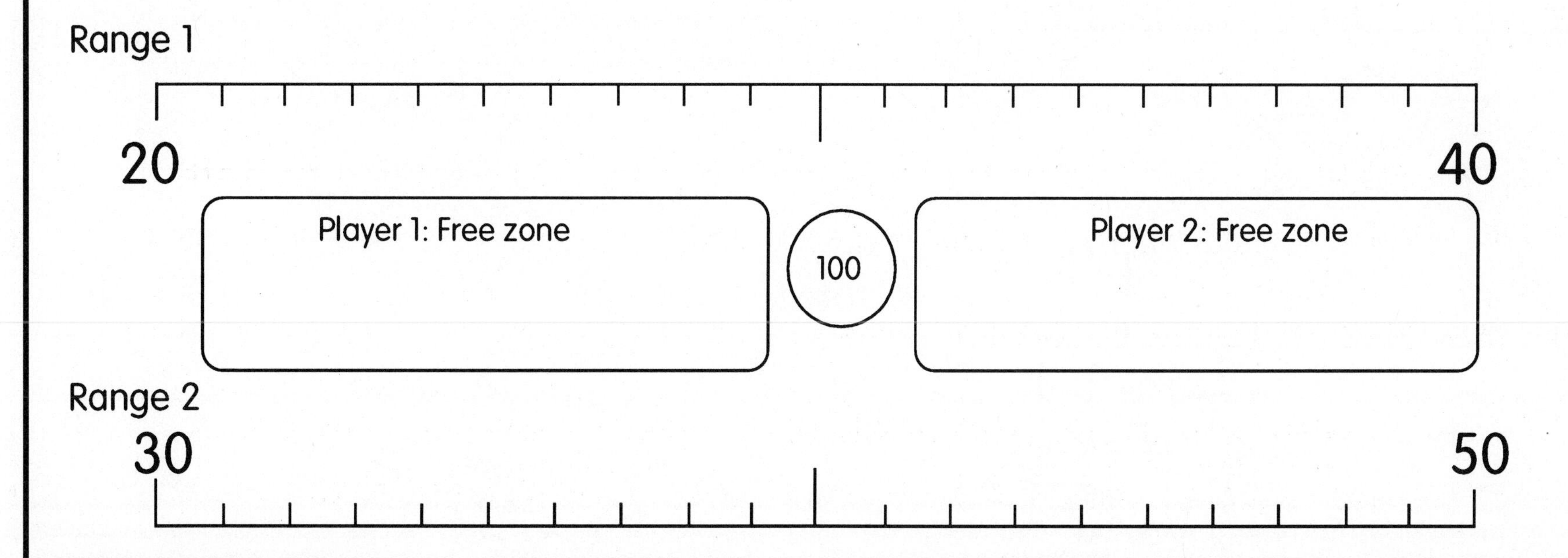

Decimal number lines

✤ Read the number marked by each arrow and use your calculator to find the total of all three numbers on each number line. Your total should match the check total.

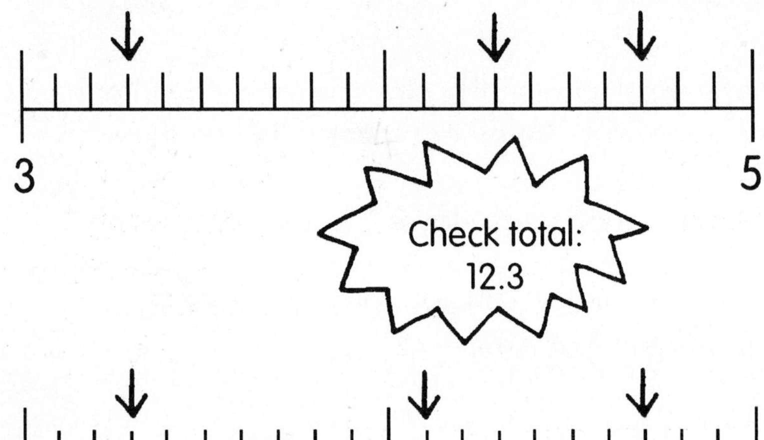

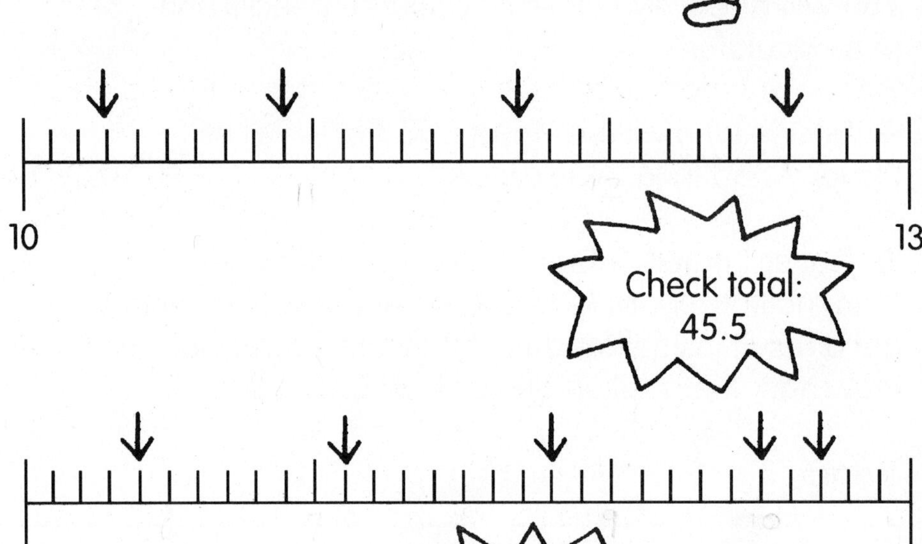

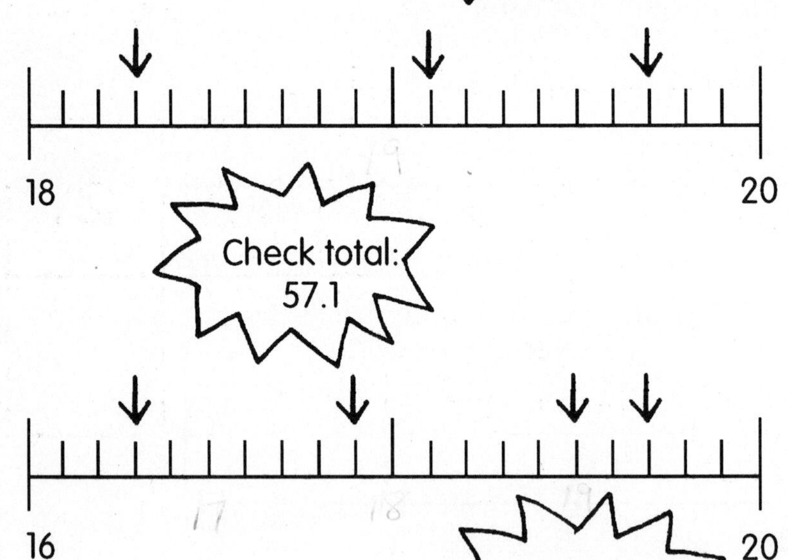

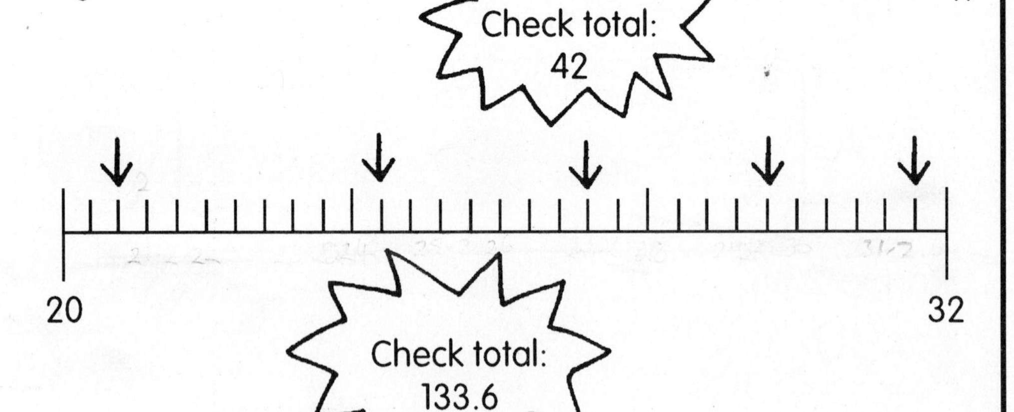

A mean puzzle

A tetromino is a shape made from four squares. A pentomino is a shape made from five squares. In each example below one number is missing. The mean of the numbers in each shape is 20.

✤ Find the missing numbers. Use a calculator to help you.

✤ Cut out the five tetrominoes and the pentomino below and try to fit them together to make a five by five square grid where each row, column and diagonal adds up to 100.

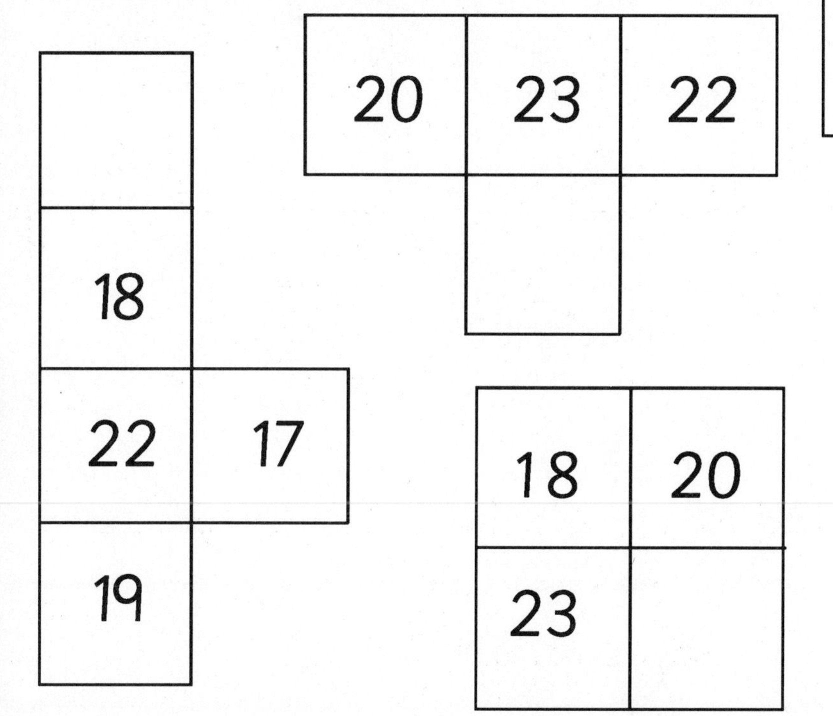

19	18		21

19	22	21

	18	17
21		

Name ______________

Heptagon angles

✤ Use a protractor to measure each angle of the first heptagon below. Use your calculator to find the total of the angles measured.

✤ Do the same for the second heptagon. Do you get nearly the same total?

✤ Draw some heptagons of your own. Measure the angles and find their total. What do you notice?

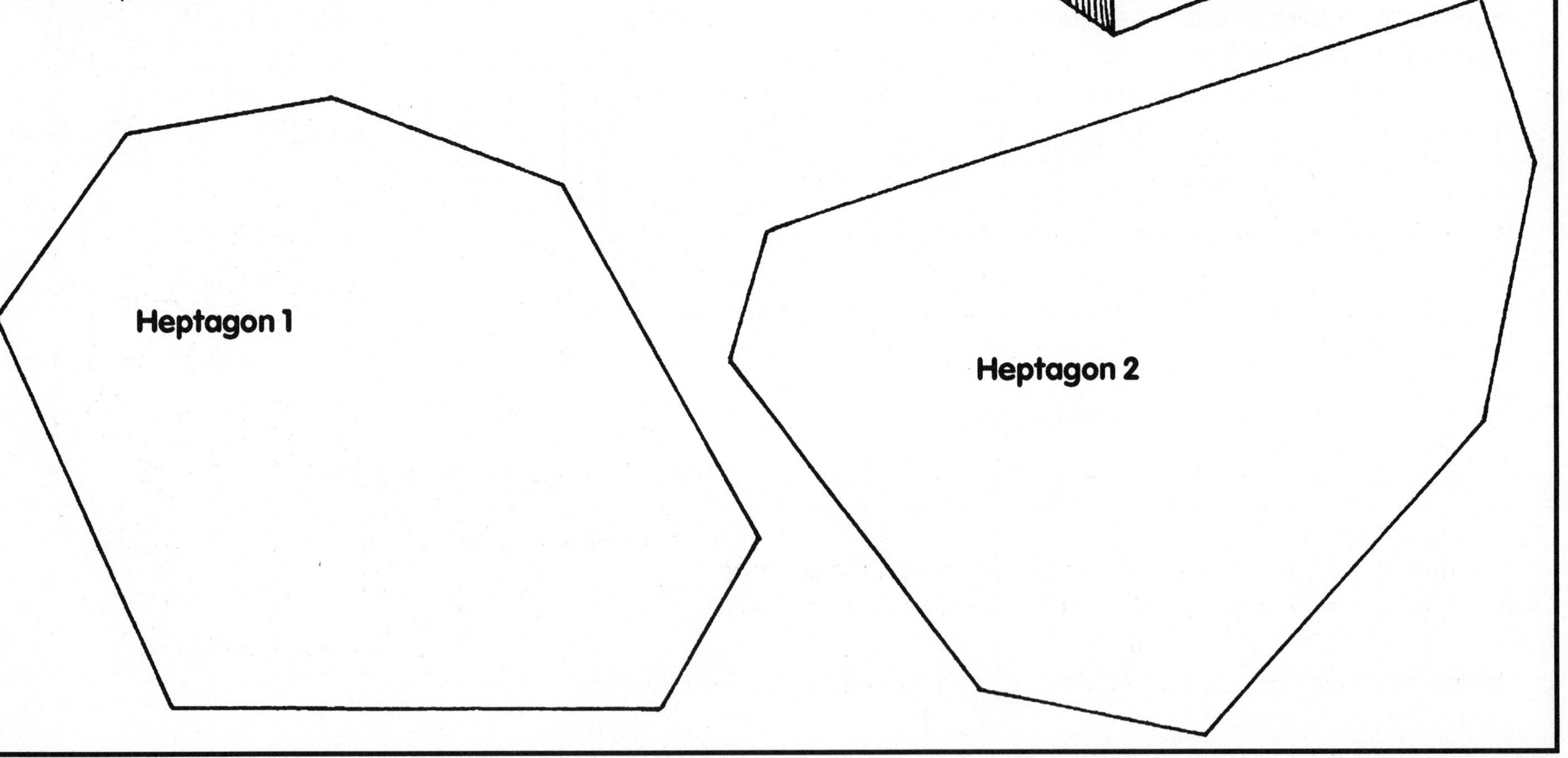

Name ____________________

A mean deal

A game for two players.

You will need: the 0 to 17 number cards, and a calculator, a pencil and a piece of paper each for scoring.

✤ Shuffle the number cards and deal five cards to each player.

✤ Each player works out the mean (the sum of the cards divided by the number of cards) and the range (the difference between the highest and lowest numbers) of their set of five numbers using their calculator.

✤ Compare your answers.

✤ Score 1 for the lower mean and 1 for the higher range.

✤ Play the game five times. The winner is the player with the higher score.

✤ What is the largest mean you can obtain with these cards?
✤ What is the lowest mean with a range of 5 you can obtain?

✤ Try changing the rules for scoring. Does this make the game fairer?

Dog data

Each of these dogs is being weighed.

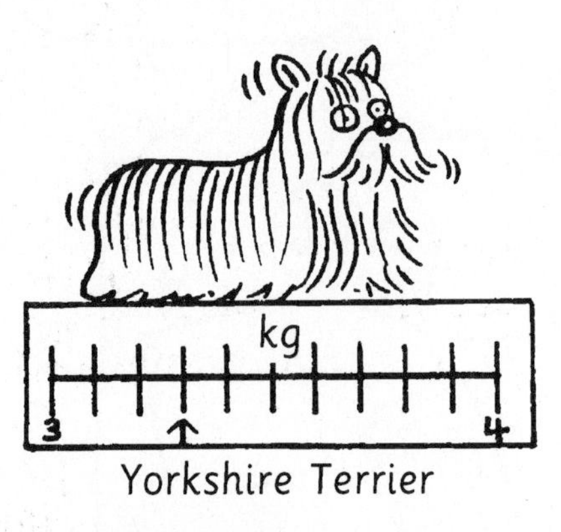

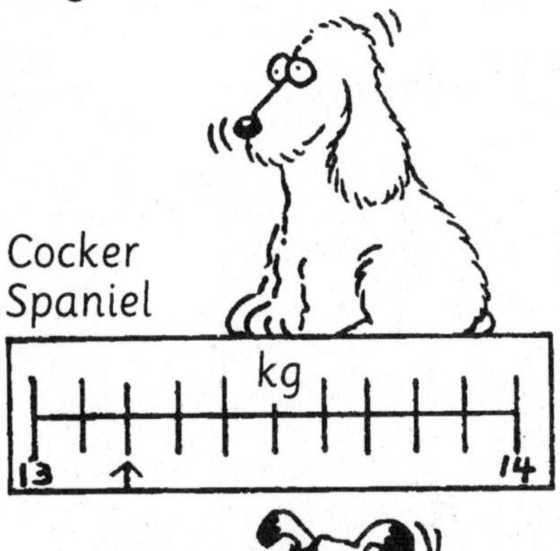

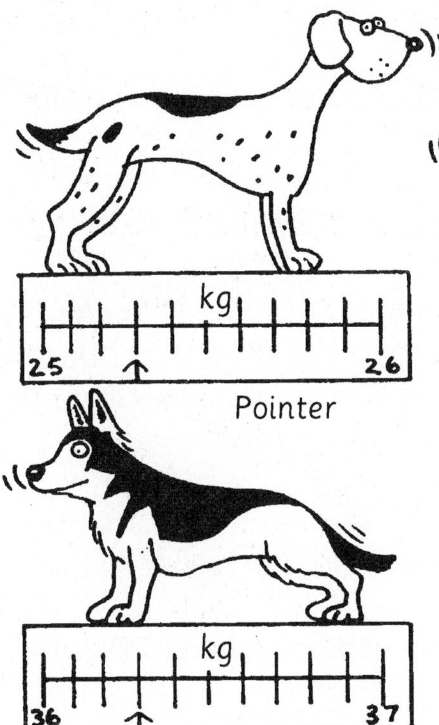

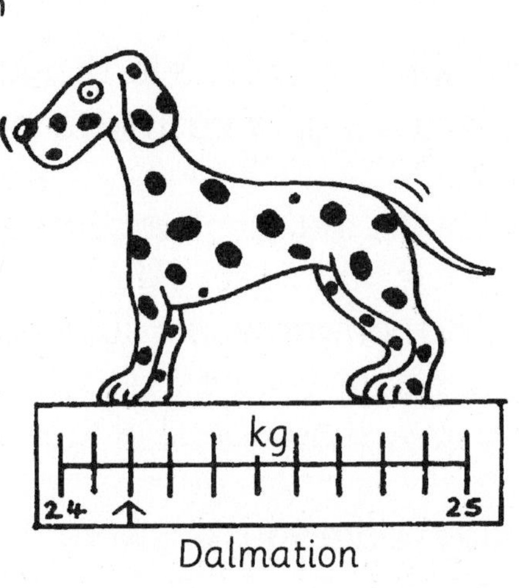

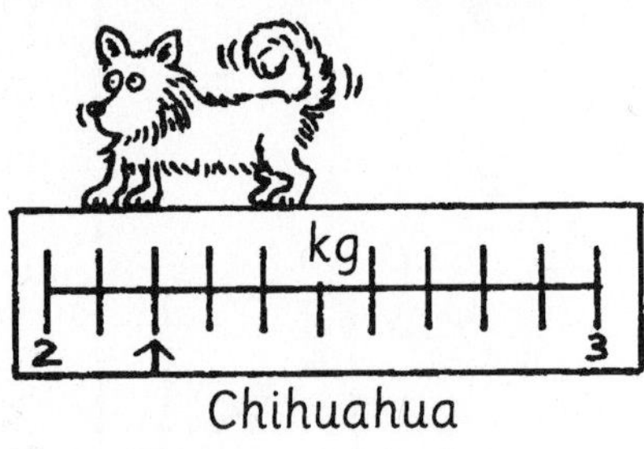

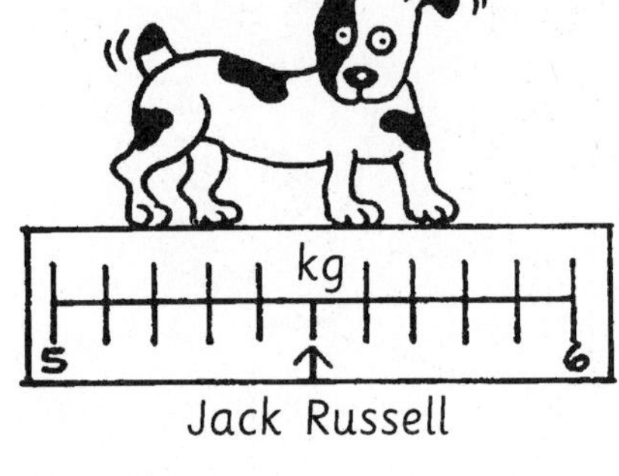

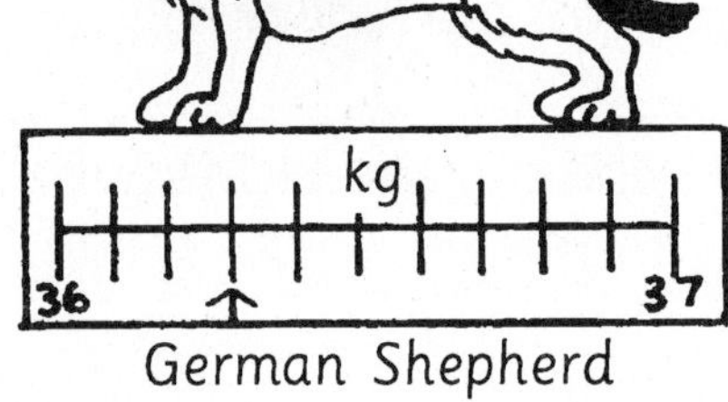

✤ Read their masses from the scales.

✤ Now use a calculator to help you to answer these questions.

- How much heavier is the heaviest dog than the lightest dog?
- Which three dogs together have a total mass of 11kg?
- Which sets of these dogs could you take on a trolley, if it can only carry 100kg?
- The Chihuahua and the Yorkshire Terrier can balance the Jack Russell on a dog see-saw. Which other arrangements of these dogs would balance each other on the see-saw?

Name ____________________

Spending for Oxfam

A recent advertisement for Oxfam showed how every £1 collected was divided up and used:

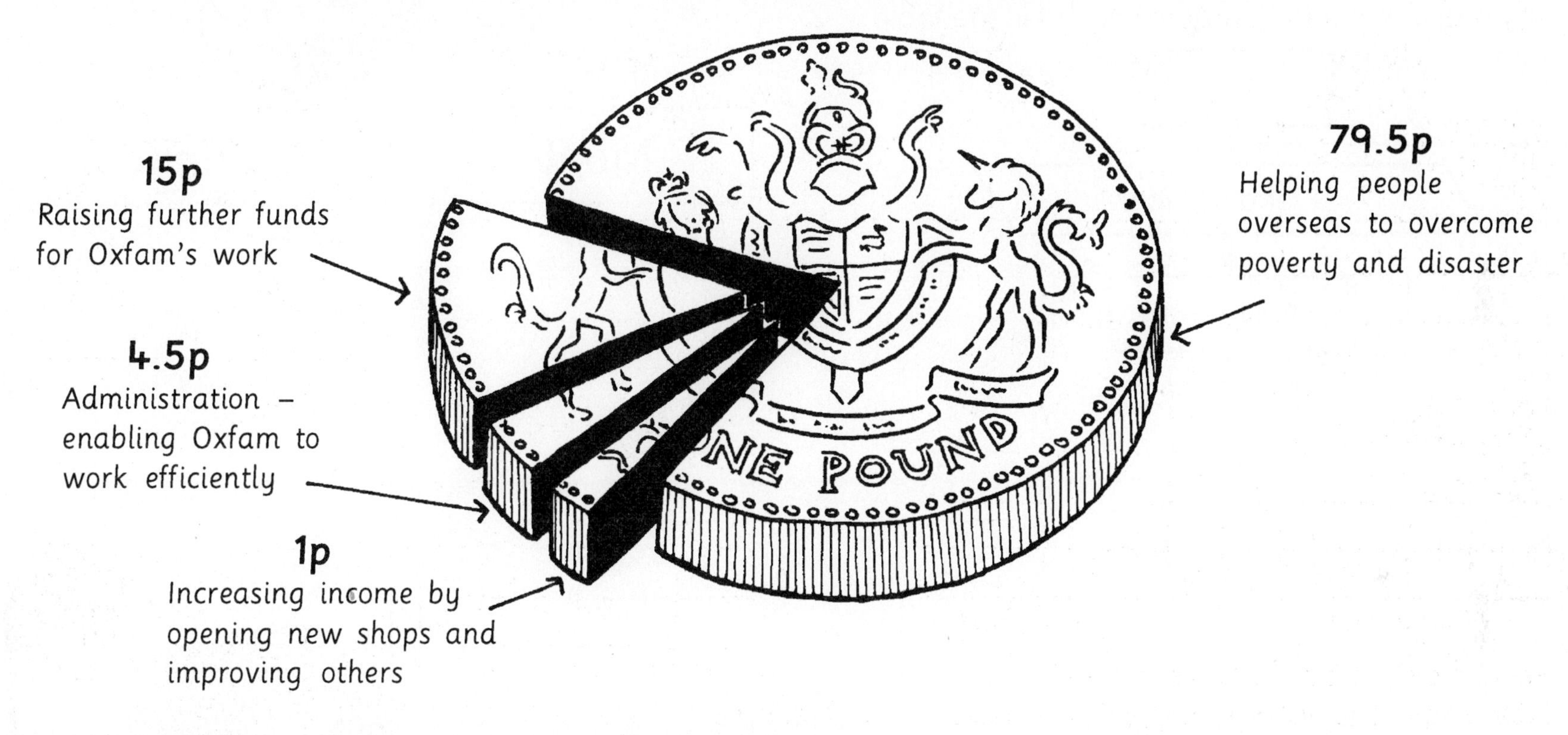

✤ Use your calculator to help you to answer these questions.

- If Oxfam spends £3 000 000 on its 'water programme' in Africa, how much money will have to be collected to pay for this part of the programme?
- An Oxfam shop needs to be redesigned. It costs £14 000 to do this and will be paid for from money collected in Wales. How much money will have to be collected in Wales in total?
- If Oxfam spends £150 000 on fund raising for a particular campaign, how much money will it have to plan to raise from the campaign?

Name ____________________

A decimal hunt

✤ Use your calculator to work through this flow chart. Record the start numbers you try and the output numbers you get in the table.

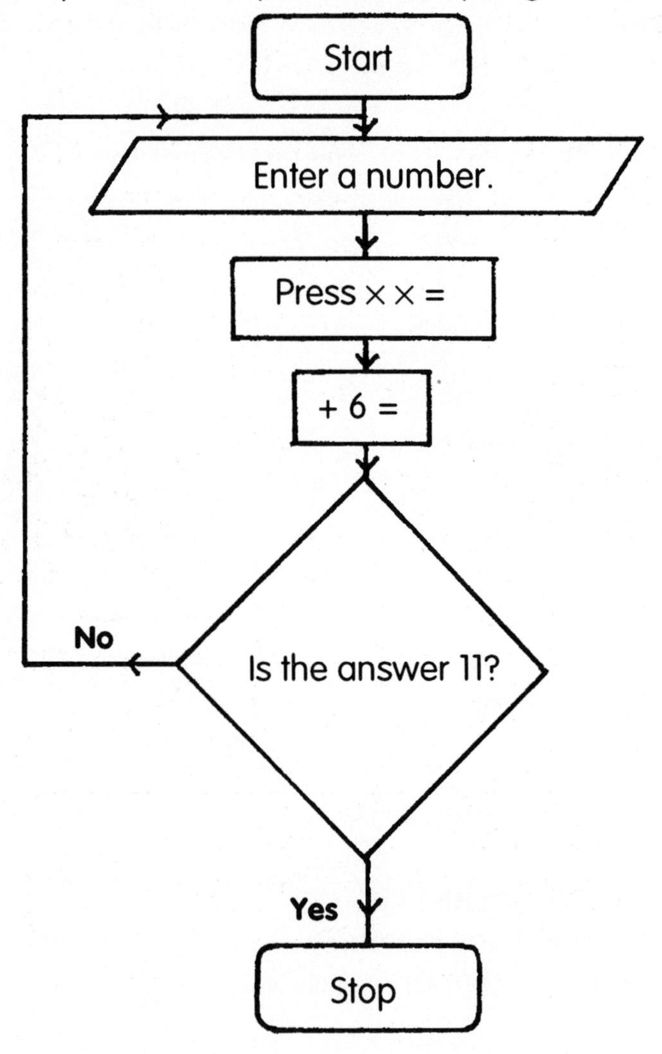

Number	Output

The Great Divider

A game for two or more players.

You will need: 24 counters, a pencil, a piece of paper as a score card and a calculator .

✤ Take turns to choose two numbers from the selection below. Divide one by the other using the calculator. You choose the order – which number to divide into which.

✤ Score according to the size of your answer.

✤ Cover the numbers you have used with counters so that they cannot be used again.

✤ The highest scorer when all the numbers have been used is 'The Great Divider'.

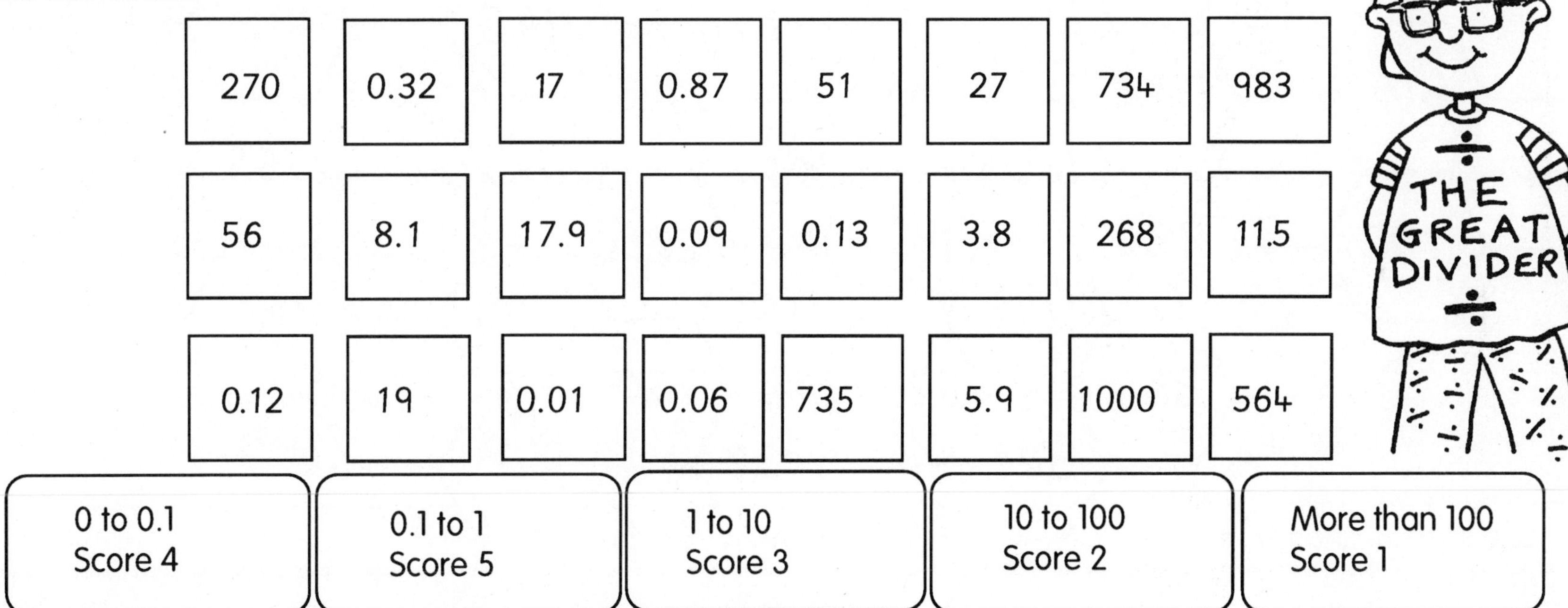

✤ What is the highest possible combined score? The lowest?

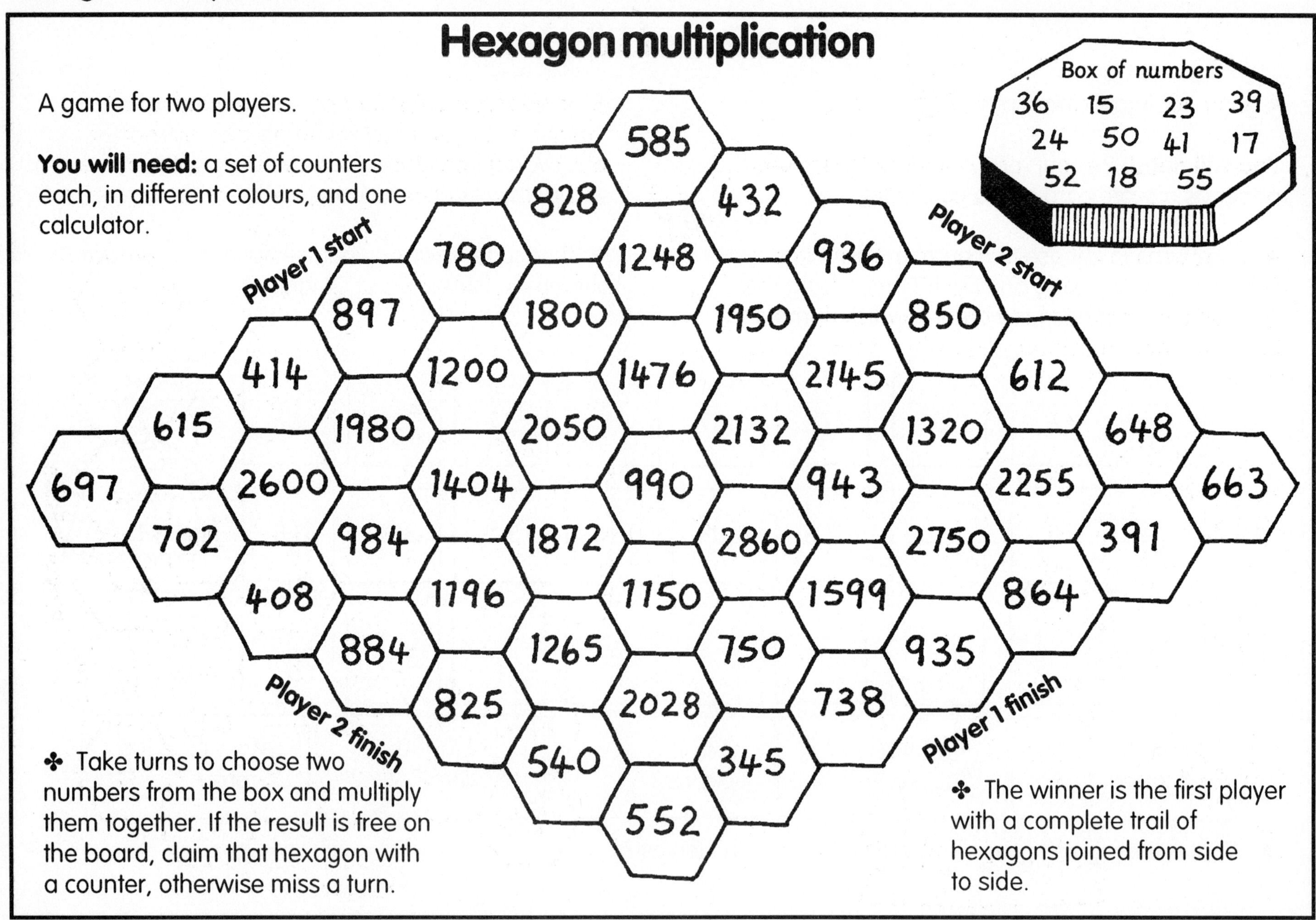
Hexagon multiplication
A game for two players.
You will need: a set of counters each, in different colours, and one calculator.
Box of numbers
36 15 23 39
24 50 41 17
52 18 55
Player 1 start
Player 2 start
Player 2 finish
Player 1 finish
585
828 432
780 1248 936
897 1800 1950 850
414 1200 1476 2145 612
615 1980 2050 2132 1320 648
697 2600 1404 990 943 2255 663
702 984 1872 2860 2750 391
408 1196 1150 1599 864
884 1265 750 935
825 2028 738
540 345
552
✤ Take turns to choose two numbers from the box and multiply them together. If the result is free on the board, claim that hexagon with a counter, otherwise miss a turn.
✤ The winner is the first player with a complete trail of hexagons joined from side to side.

Name ____________________

Honeycomb division

A game for two players.

You will need: a set of counters each, in different colours, and one calculator.

✤ Choose who will go first and then take turns.

✤ Each player states which hexagon number they are trying to calculate, and then chooses one number from each box and divides one by the other.

✤ If the result is the number in the nominated hexagon, a counter is placed on the hexagon. If not, miss a turn. The winner is the first player with a complete trail of hexagons joined from side to side.

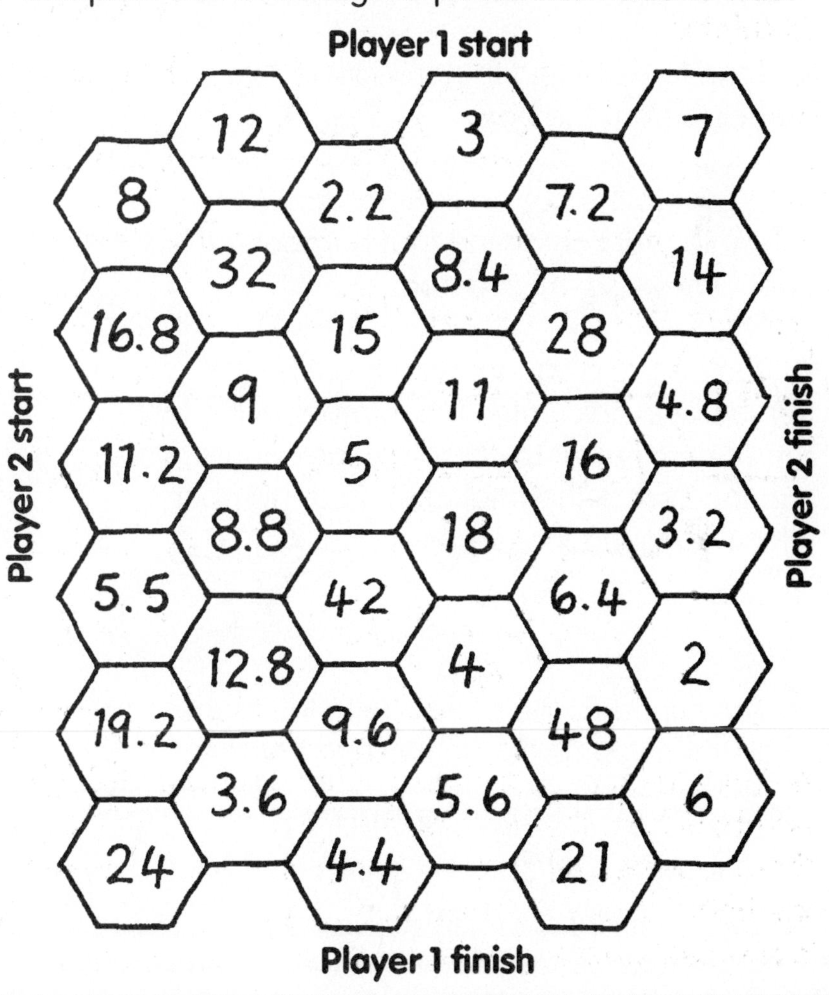

Name ____________________

Square capture

A game for two players.

You will need: a different coloured pencil each and a calculator.

✤ Take turns to find the product of two numbers from the box.

✤ Colour in the bar on the diagram (for example 198) containing that number – if it is free! Otherwise, miss a turn.

✤ To capture a square, you must be the person who calculates the number in the last bar and colours it to complete the square. You can then score the total of the four numbers which surround that square.

✤ The winner is the person with the highest total when you decide to finish the game.

Box of numbers

12 14 22 18 16 20 13 17 11 19 21 15

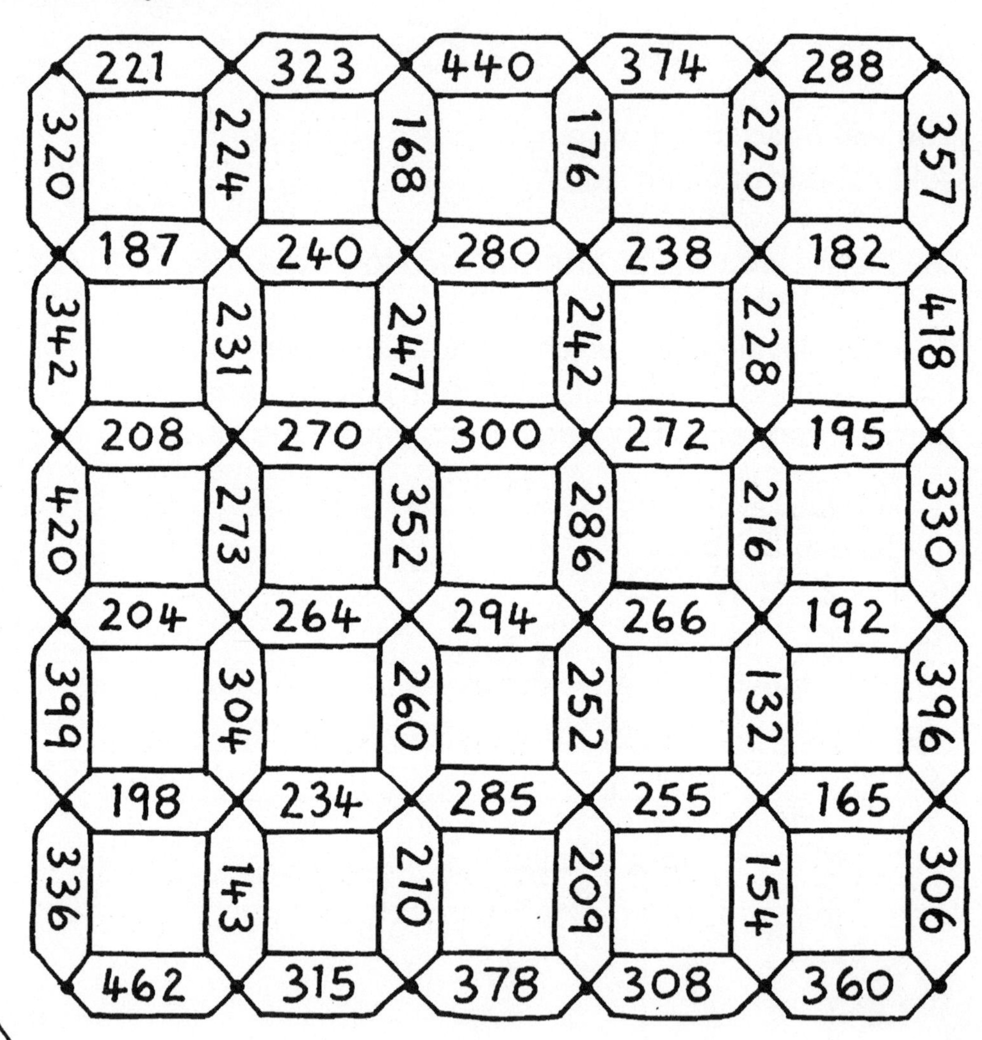

Name ____________________

Heartbeats

35 heartbeats per minute
Average life span 24 years

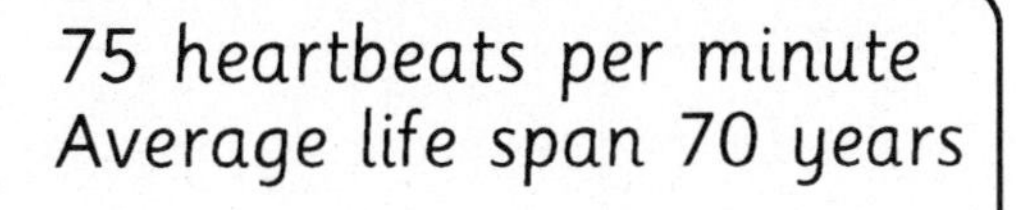

115 heartbeats per minute
Average life span 15 years

328 heartbeats per minute
Average life span 2.5 years

✤ Use your calculator to help you to answer these questions.
How many times does each animal's heart beat (on average):

- in an hour?
- in a week?
- in a month?

✤ How many times will your heart beat in a week?

Name ____________________

Fractions and decimals

You may be able to change fractions to decimals using your calculator if it has a F▶D key. Otherwise you will need to enter the fraction with the top (the numerator) and bottom (the denominator) numbers separated by the division sign. (The numerator divided by the denominator.)

For example: to change $\frac{1}{4}$ to a decimal press:

1 ÷ 4 =

✤ Change these fractions to decimals:

$\frac{2}{5} =$ ☐ $\frac{6}{10} =$ ☐ $\frac{40}{100} =$ ☐ $\frac{6}{9} =$ ☐ $\frac{5}{9} =$ ☐ $\frac{2}{3} =$ ☐

$\frac{1}{8} =$ ☐ $\frac{125}{1000} =$ ☐ $\frac{2}{8} =$ ☐ $\frac{7}{28} =$ ☐ $\frac{6}{24} =$ ☐ $\frac{8}{16} =$ ☐ $\frac{10}{40} =$ ☐

$\frac{25}{45} =$ ☐ $\frac{3}{16} =$ ☐ $\frac{5}{8} =$ ☐ $\frac{3}{5} =$ ☐ $\frac{90}{120} =$ ☐ $\frac{7}{14} =$ ☐ $\frac{13}{26} =$ ☐

✤ Do any of the fractions above have the same decimal answers? If so, try to explain why.

✤ Find as many fractions as you can which give you these decimals:

0.25 0.5 0.16 0.35

Range roulette

A game for up to four players.

You will need: the roulette board opposite with the pointer or a plastic spinning arrow, a different-coloured counter for each player and a calculator.

How to play

✣ Decide in which order to play and place your counter on the starting number by your position.

✣ Take turns to spin the pointer/ arrow to find the required **range** for a product. Use the calculator to multiply the number your counter is on by any other number you choose to get a result in the range shown by the pointer.

✣ If the result is in the required range, move two places clockwise. If the result is in a neighbouring range (on either side of the chosen range), move one place clockwise.

✣ The winner is the first person to complete a circuit.

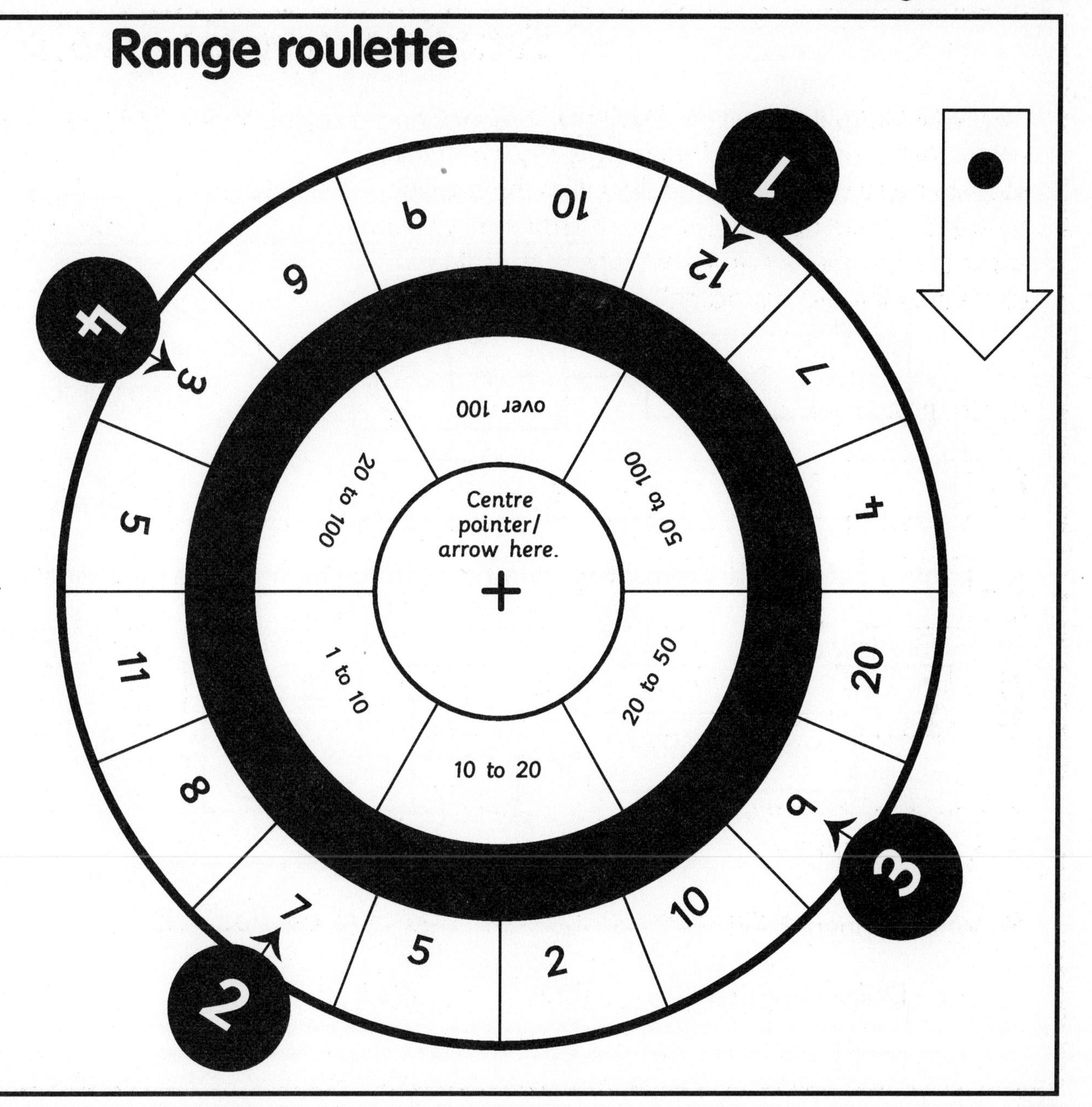

Name ____________________

Keep pressing

You will need: the multiplication grid, a pencil and a calculator.

✤ Use your calculator and follow the instructions in this flow chart:

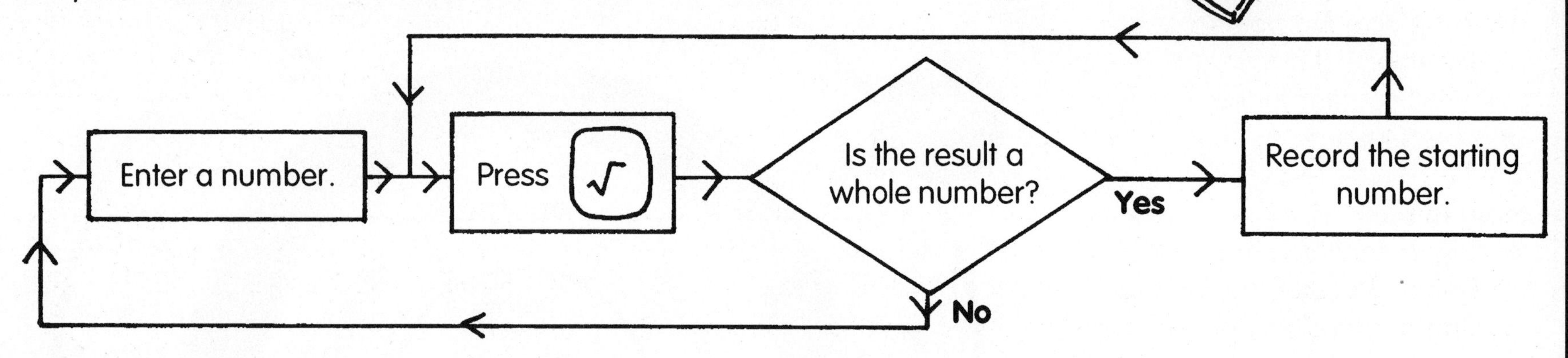

✤ What sort of numbers give whole numbers? Shade them on the multiplication grid.

✤ Try this flow chart:

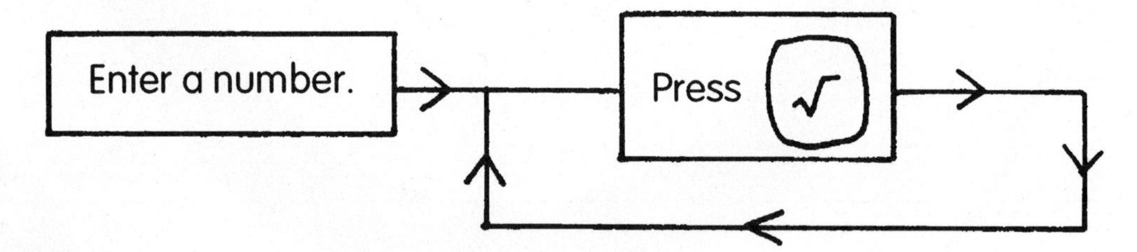

✤ What happens?

✤ Will it always happen?

Name ____________________

Rush to estimate

A game for two or more players and a referee.

You will need: the set of price label cards, a pencil and paper for each player and a stop-watch and a calculator for the referee.

✤ The referee should shuffle the cards, deal four face down and then turn them over so everyone can see the prices and start the stop-watch.

✤ Within 30 seconds, the players must write down an estimate of the total of the four prices to the nearest pound.

✤ The referee then adds up the prices using the calculator and corrects the total to the nearest pound, and checks the other players' results and award points:

- those players with the same value as the referee win 3 points;
- those players with a value which is £1 more or less win 2 points;
- those players with a value which is £2 more or less win 1 point.

✤ Play five rounds. The winner is the one with the highest score.

Name ____________________

Breathing

When a whale or dolphin breathes out, it blows out a mist of oily water vapour from its blow hole. Whales and dolphins breathe at different rates at different times. The dots on the two graphs below show the number of blows per minute and the time spent swimming on the surface or diving under water.

This shows six blows per minute for five minutes, i.e., 30 blows.

Dolphin

Surface

0 5 10 15 20 25 30 35 40 45 50 minutes

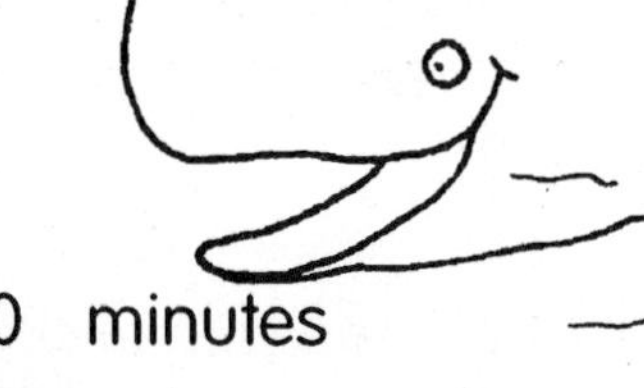

Sperm whale

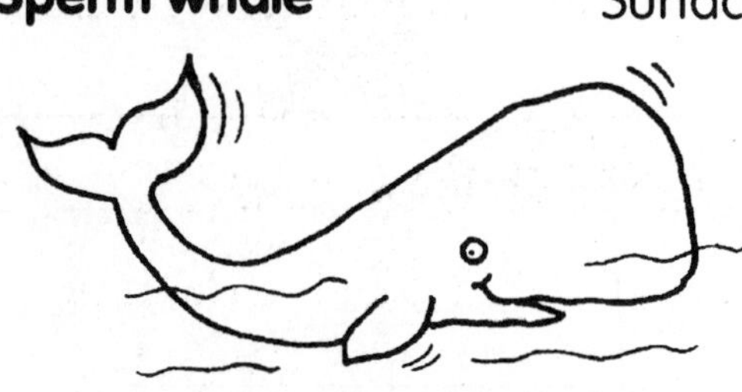

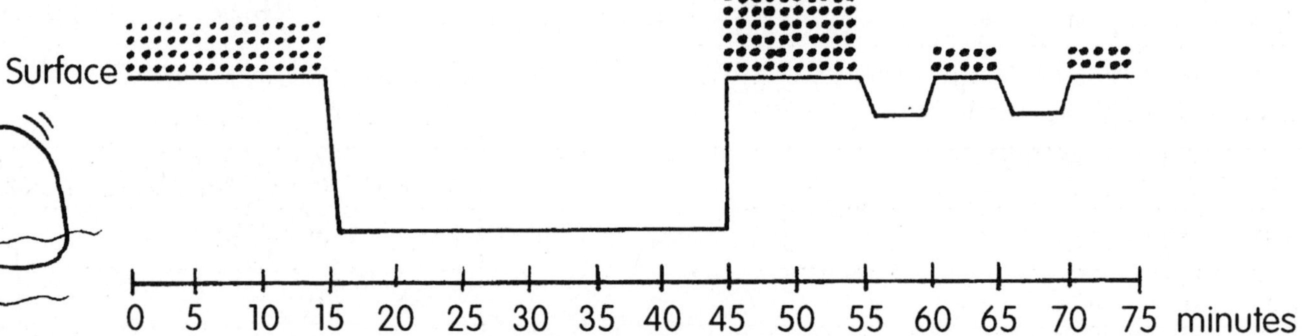

✤ Approximately how many times do the dolphin and the whale breathe in an hour, a day, a week and a month? Use your calculator to help you to work this out.

✤ Now find a way to calculate how often you breathe in an hour, a day, a week and a month. How often have you breathed since you were born?

Name ____________________

Communications

✤ Approximately, how many televisions, radios and newspapers are there in each country? Use a calculator to help you to work this out.

✤ What else can you say about the communications?

Country	Population (millions)	% Urban
Australia	16.9	85
Brazil	150.4	75
India	844	27
Japan	123.8	77
UK	57.4	92
USA	249.2	74

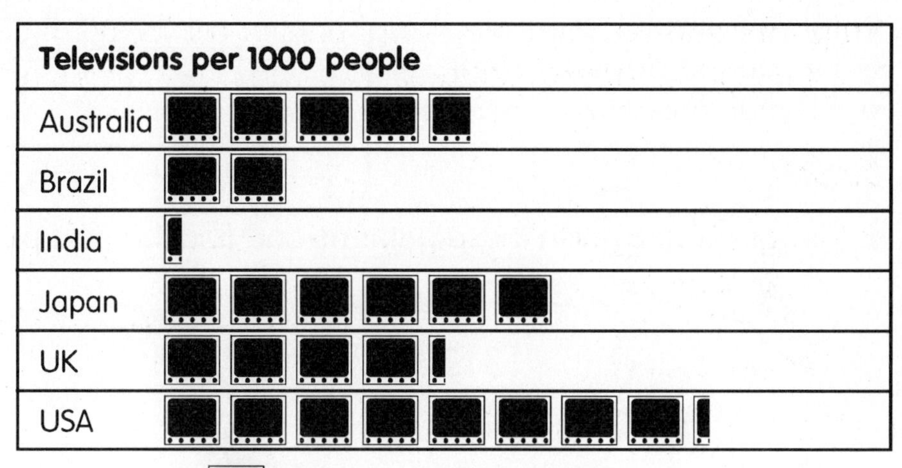

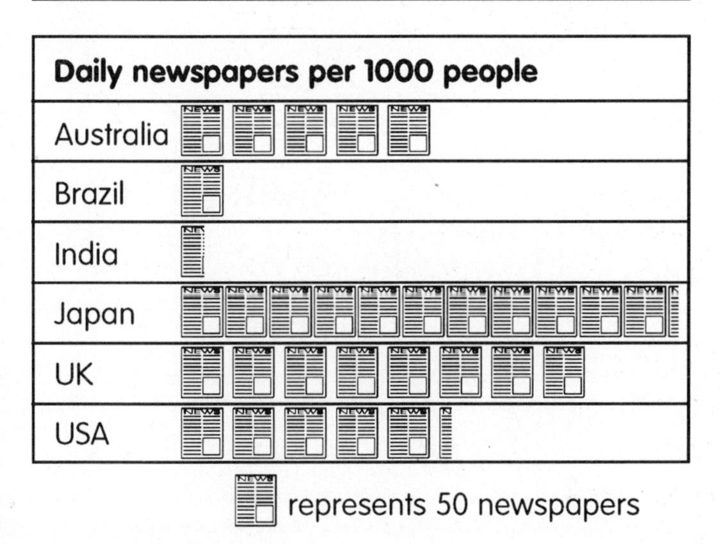

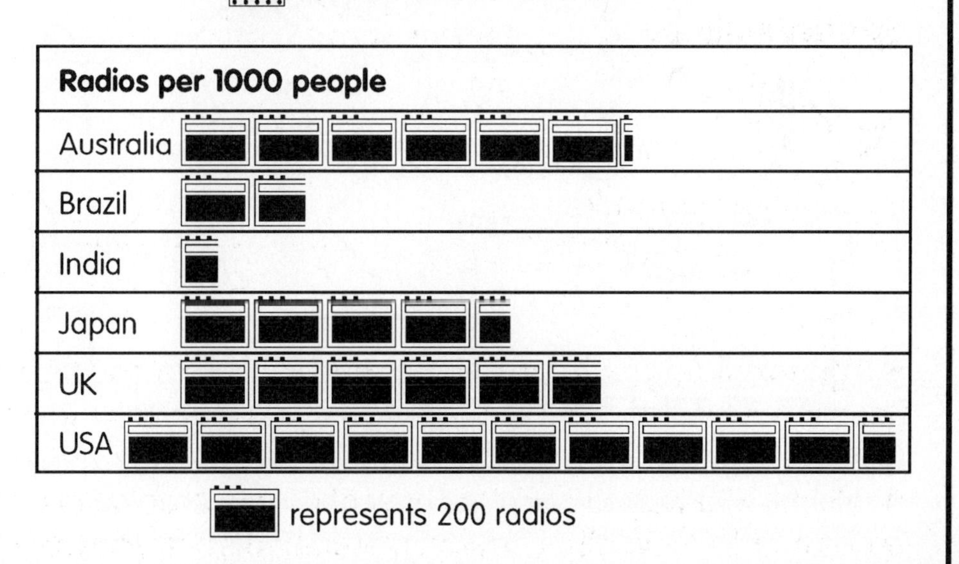

Name ______________

Lots of patterns

For this activity you may want more than one calculator.

- Fill your display with 121212...
- Fill your display with 2323...
- Fill your display with 3434...
- Find the next patterns.

1414...
2525...

1212...
2424...
3...

- Fill your display with these patterns and find the next patterns in each set:

1313...
2424...

321321...
432432...

1212...
123123...
12341...

1919...
2828...
3737...

12312...
2342...

3131...
4242...

10101...
2020...

9898...
8787...
7676...

12345123...
234562...

- Design some sets of patterns of your own. Try to explain them in words.

Name ____________________

Arithmagon

You will need: the 1 to 6 number cards and a calculator.

✤ Put the cards on to the diagram so that each line has the same total. Use your calculator to help you.

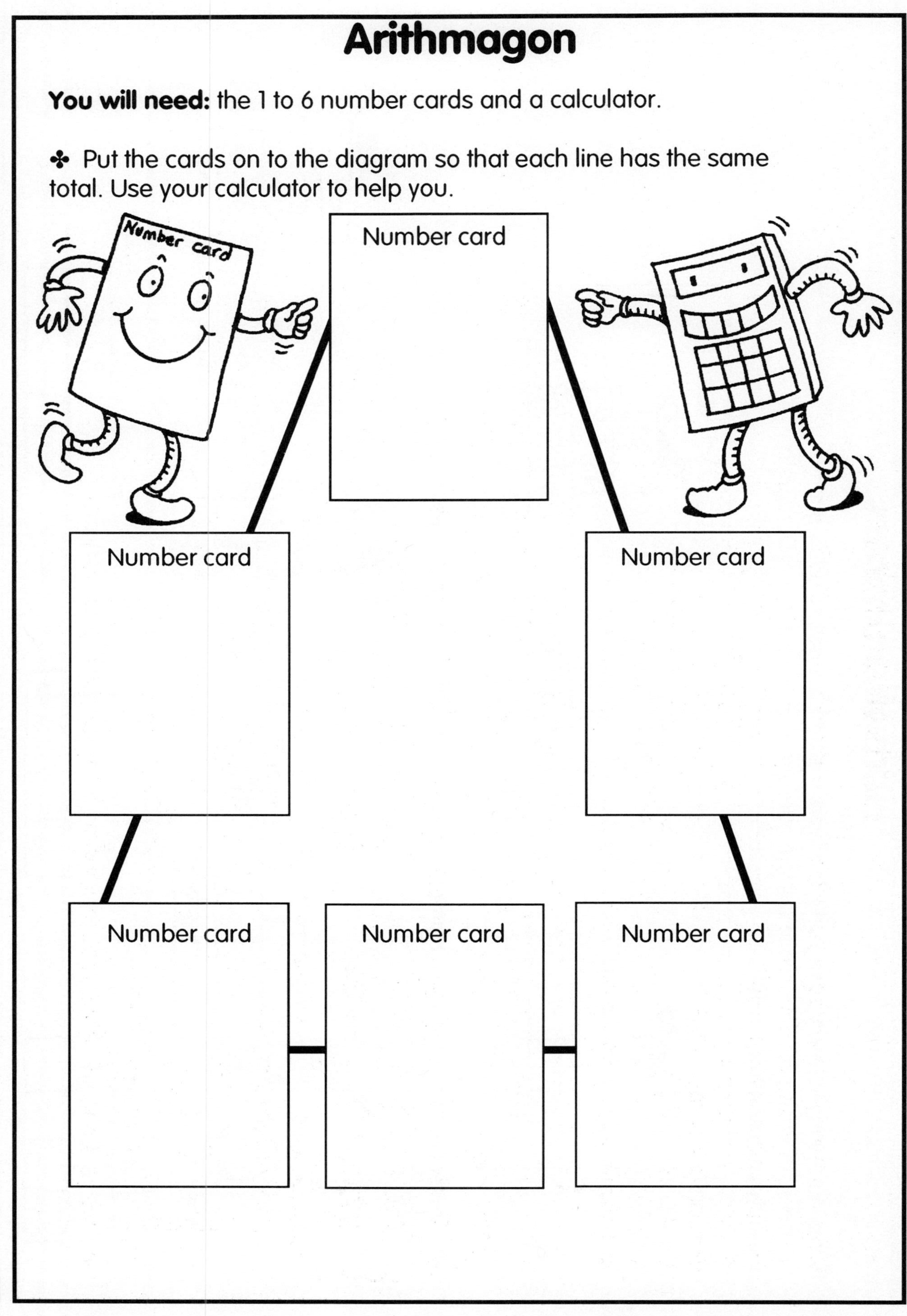

Name ____________________

Humpty numbers

What number is Humpty sitting on? You work the number out by adding the numbers in each pair of bricks to get the number above. So in the picture below Humpty will be sitting on 19.

✤ Find some of the numbers Humpty might be sitting on in each of these walls.
A calculator will be helpful here.

Name ______________

Hopscotch

A game for two players.

You will need: a counter and a calculator each.

✤ Take turns to move from slab to slab of the hopscotch grid until you reach the end.

✤ To move to the next slab you must add on the correct number so that your calculator display shows the number on the slab. You may not use the clear/cancel key.

✤ Where there is a double slab you may choose which way to go. If you make a mistake, try to correct it next go.

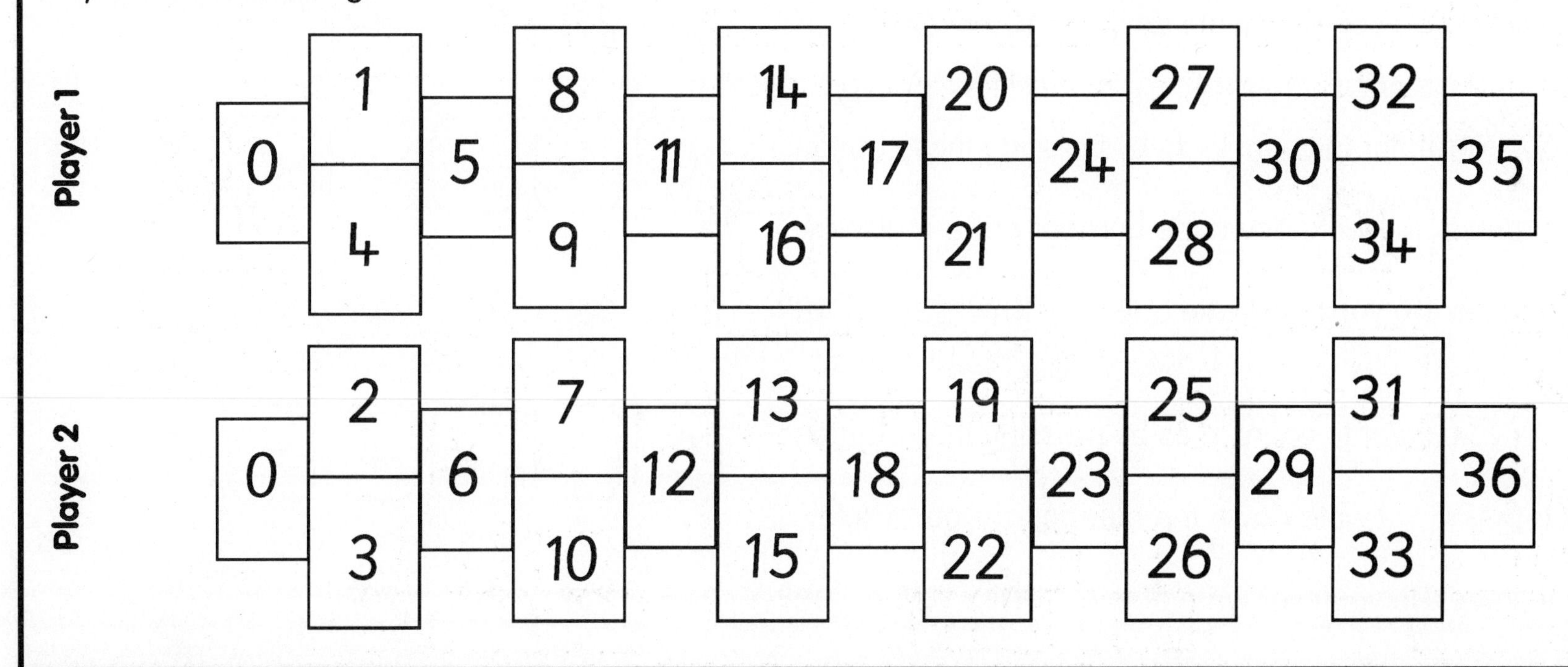

Name ____________________

Constant counting

✤ Set up your calculator to count in 2s by pressing these buttons:   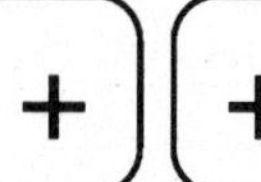 [+] [=] [0]

Each time you press [=] write down the number on your display.

Try this lots of times. Do you ever write down: **10? 25? 19? 22? 36? 21? 20?**

✤ Set up your calculator to count in 3s by pressing these buttons: [C] [3] [+] [+] [=] [0]

Each time you press [=] write down the number on your display.

Try this lots of times. Do you ever write down: **10? 25? 19? 22? 36? 21? 20?**

✤ Set up your calculator to count in 4s by pressing these buttons: [C] [4] [+] [+] [=] [0]

Each time you press [=] write down the number on your display.

Try this lots of times. Do you ever write down: **10? 25? 19? 22? 36? 21? 20?**

✤ Set up your calculator to count in 5s by pressing these buttons: [C] [5] [+] [+] [=] [0]

Each time you press [=] write down the number on your display.

Try this lots of times. Do you ever write down: **10? 25? 19? 22? 36? 21? 20?**

Counting backwards

✤ Set up your calculator to count backwards from 50 by pressing these buttons:

What happens as soon as you press [=] ? And again [=] ?

Stop at 23, what will the next number be? Write it down.

Stop again at 16, predict the next number. Were you right?
Keep going. What happens?

✤ Count backwards from another number, try to predict each number before you press [=].

✤ Try counting backwards in 2s from 23:

Do you go through 0?

✤ Try counting backwards from different numbers.
Write down those numbers which allow you to go through 0.

✤ Try counting backwards in different steps.
When do you get similar patterns in the positive and negative numbers?

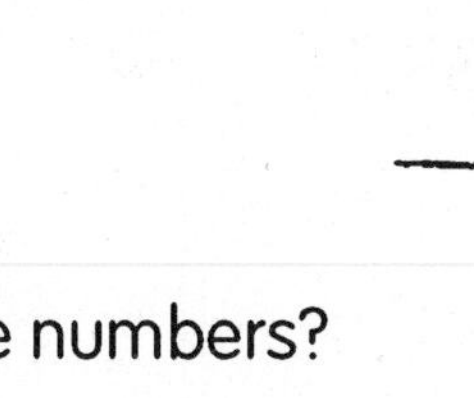

Name ____________________

Five, four, three, two, one

- Cut out these cards.
- Make up some sums using all the digits once only.
- Use your calculator to find all the possible answers you can.
- You may use as many of the + cards as you wish.

For example: 1 + 2 + 3 + 4 + 5 = ? or 312 + 45 = ?

Name ____________________

Mystery boxes

With a calculator, you can change 2 into 18 by using different operations.

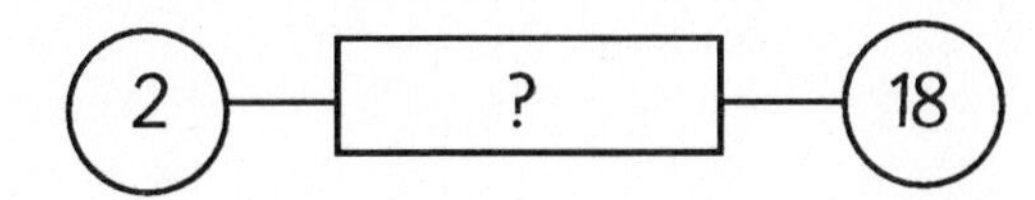

In the mystery box there could be: + 16,
or: + 20 – 4,
or: + 2 + 2 + 2 + 2 + 2 + 2 + 2 + 2,
or: × 8 + 2,
or: × 20 – 4 ÷ 2,
or: × 19 – 20.

✤ Find several possible operations which could be in these mystery boxes.

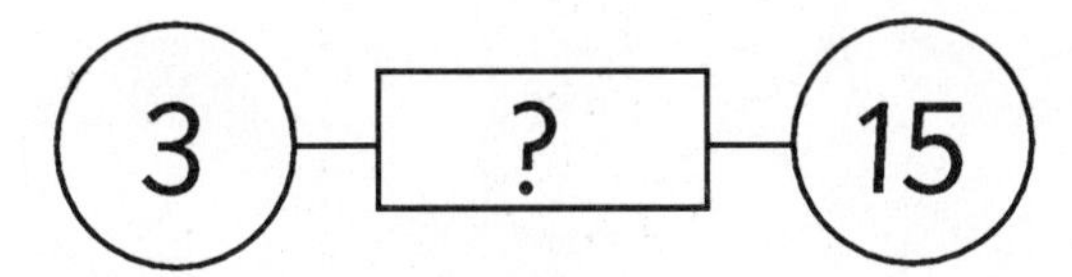

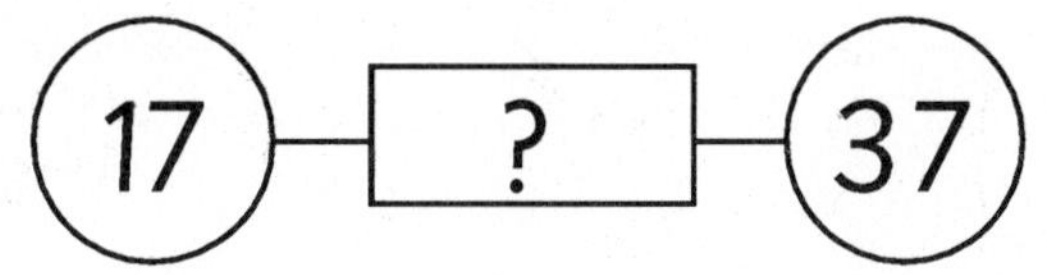

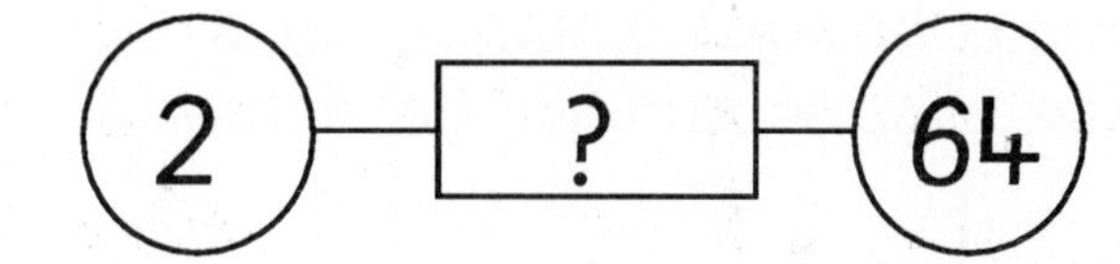

7 — ? — 21

20 — ? — 50

18 — ? — 5

9 — ? — 25

3 — ? — 51

111 — ? — 3

Name ____________________

Doubling

- Set up your calculator to double by pressing these buttons:

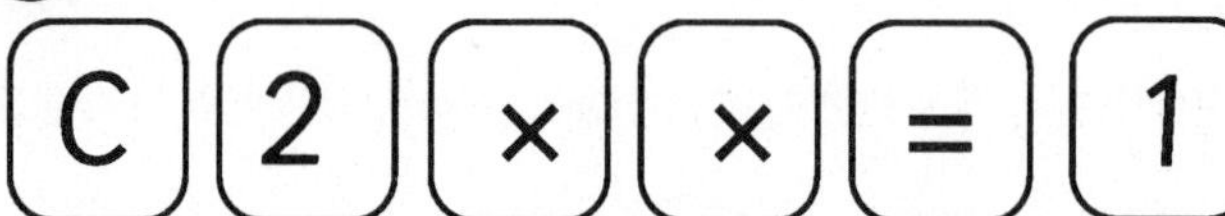

- Enter a number and press [=] and see what happens.

- Find and write down some pairs of numbers like this:

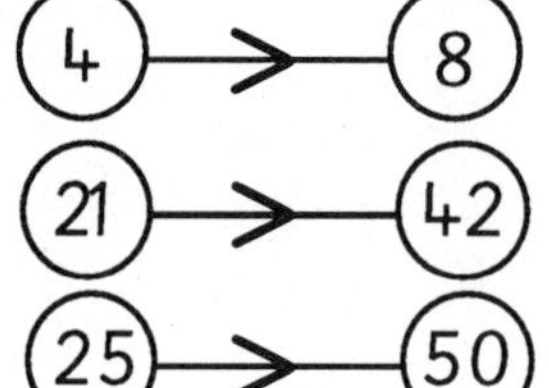

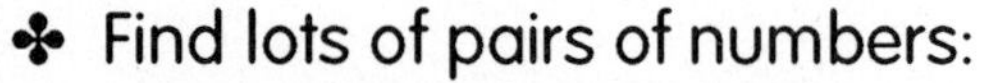

- Find lots of pairs of numbers:
- where the second number ends in 0 (like the last example above);
- where the second number ends in 6;
- where the second number ends in 1.

- Play this game with a partner.

You will need: the 6 number grid, a set of counters each and a calculator.

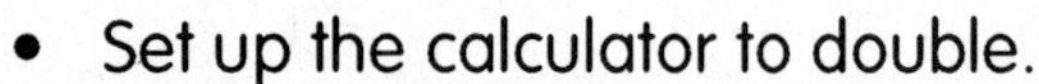

- Set up the calculator to double.
- Choose who will go first. Then take turns to choose an uncovered target number from the grid and then enter any other number on to the calculator and press [=] .
- If the target number comes up on the display, you can capture that square with one of your counters.
- If you do not get the target number, that is the end of your turn. Do NOT press [C] .
- The winner is the first person with three of their counters in a row.

Name ____________________

Halving

✤ Set up your calculator to halve numbers by pressing these buttons:

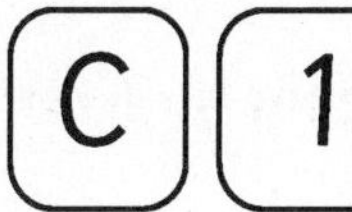

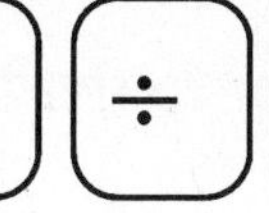

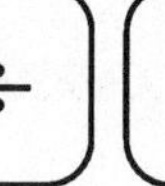

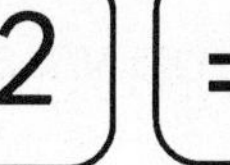

✤ Enter 64 and press [=]. Write down the result.

✤ Press [=] again. Write down the result.

✤ Enter these numbers and press [=]. Write down the pairs like this:
Which numbers give you whole number results?

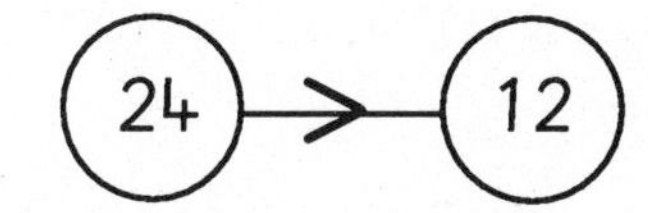

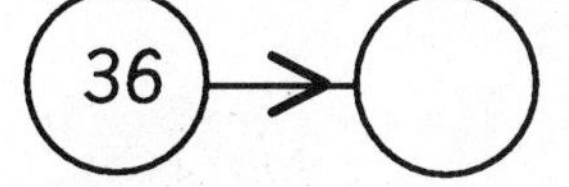

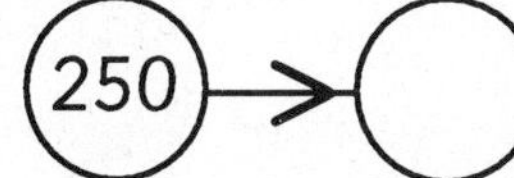

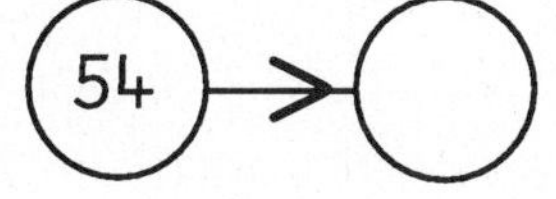

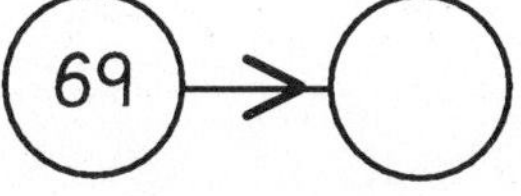

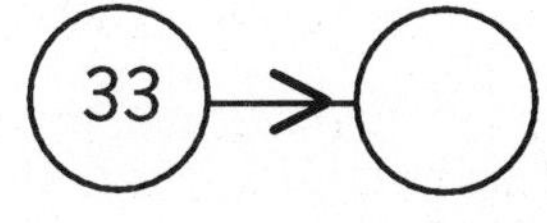

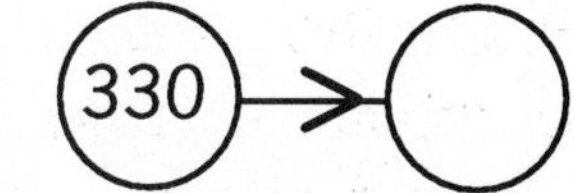

✤ What numbers will you have to enter so that the result when you press [=] will be:

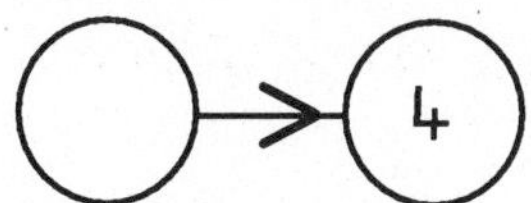

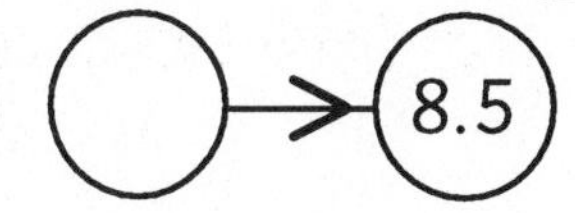

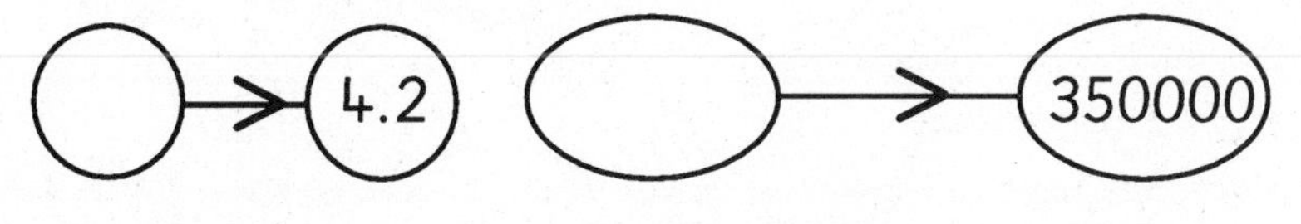

✤ What number will you have to begin with if you keep on halving and after five presses of [=] you finish with 3?

Name ____________________

Multiplying by 10

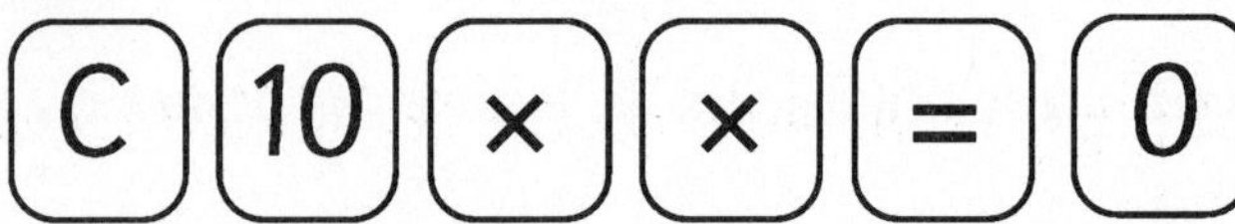

✤ Set up your calculator to multiply by 10 by pressing these buttons: C 10 × × = 0

- Write down a number, and then enter it on to your calculator. Each time you press = write down the results. Do this lots of times. Write down what you notice.

- Use these numbers as starting numbers. What do you notice?

2.34 189.1 12.765 67.346 800.02 273 1890 38.54

What is the difference between what happens with numbers with decimal points and those without? Try to write a rule which works for all numbers when you multiply by 10.

✤ Write down some numbers. Predict the results when you multiply them by 10. Then check by using your calculator.

✤ Try these ideas again, but multiply by 100 and then by 1000.

Name ____________________

Decimal discoverer

✤ Set up your calculator to divide by 10 by pressing these buttons: [C] [0] [÷] [÷] [10] [=] [0]

✤ Write down a number, and then enter it on to your calculator. Each time you press [=] write down the results. Do this lots of times. Write down what you notice.

✤ How many times, after you have entered the number, do you need to press [=] in order to change:

- 2345.78 into 2.34578?
- 12345.6 into 1.23456?
- 3456734 into 3.456734?
- 82736.459 into 82.736459?

✤ What number would you need to enter to obtain 2.17359 with:

- three presses of [=] after setting up the calculator?
- two presses?
- four presses?
- five presses?
- six presses?

✤ Try the previous question again with:
3.456, 9.56 , 3.1425, 7.258, 6.1, 4, 34.56, 95.8, 31.425, 72.58, 61, 40.

✤ Try with some other sets of numbers. Write down what you have noticed.

✤ Try dividing numbers by 100, do similar things happen?
What about dividing by 0.1? Do you get similar results?

Name ________________

Steps to 100

✤ Use the constant on your calculator to find out what numbers you can use to count up to 100. For example: 2 + + = . Record your results carefully on a diagram like the one shown below. Try using different numbers for your constant. How many ways can you find?

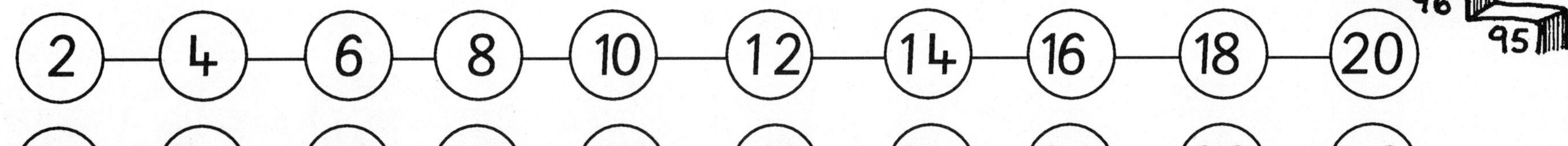

42 — 44 — 46 — 48 — 50 — 52 — 54 — 56 — 58 — 60

62 — 64 — 66 — 68 — 70 — 72 — 74 — 76 — 78 — 80

82 — 84 — 86 — 88 — 90 — 92 — 94 — 96 — 98

100

Name ____________________

What answers?

✤ Cut out these cards and use them to make up some sums. You may use as many of the cards as you wish.

✤ Use your calculator to work out the results.

17	2	9	12	3
–	–	–	+	=

Name ____________

Line abacus numbers

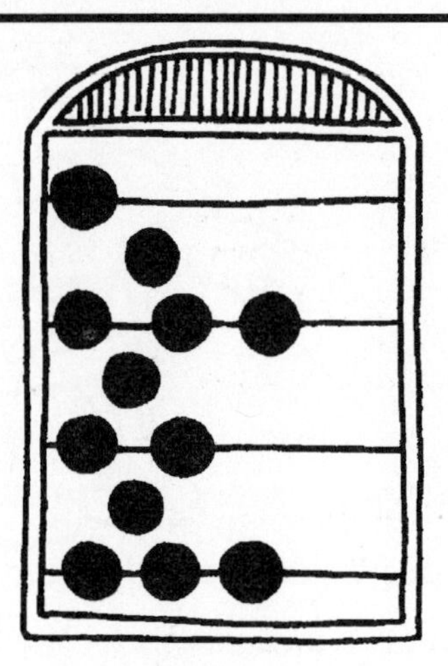

The counters on the line abacus opposite represent numbers. This example uses 12 counters to show:

1000 + 500 + 300 + 50 + 20 + 5 + 3 = 1878

✣ Use your calculator to help you to work out these numbers which also use 12 counters:

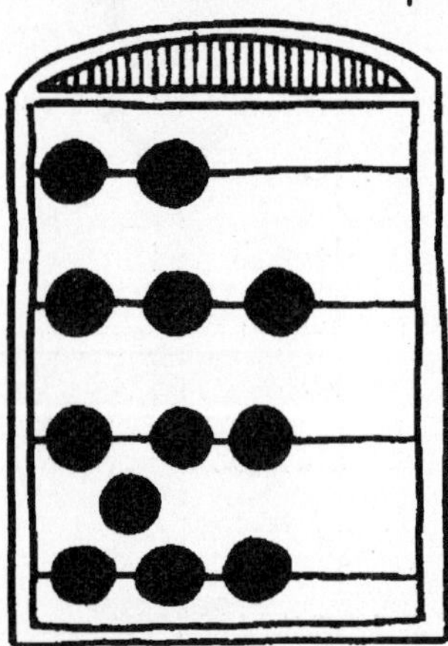

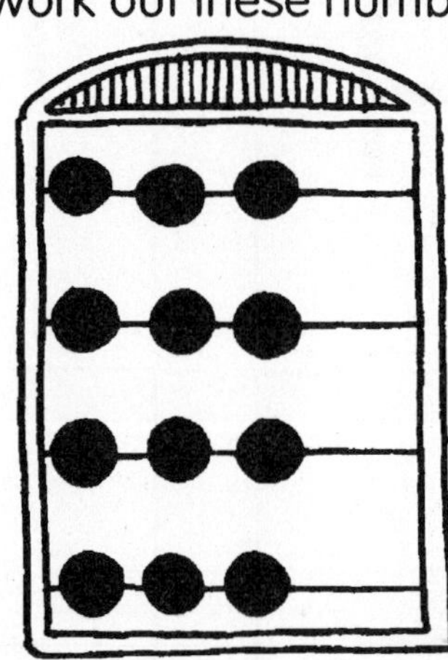

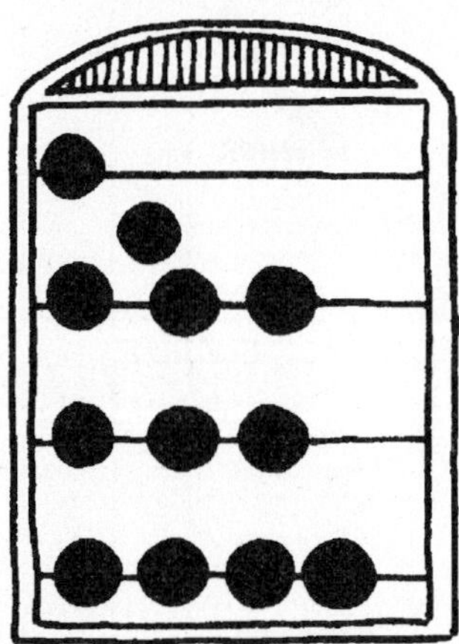

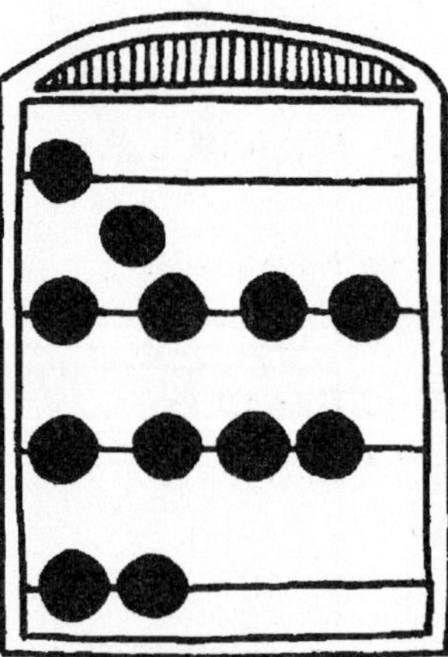

You will need: the line abacus page, some counters and a calculator.

- ✣ What other numbers can you make using 12 counters?
- ✣ What numbers can you make using three counters?
- ✣ What numbers can you make using five counters?

Number word rollers: 1

You will need: scissors, adhesive, a pencil, paper for scoring and a calculator.

✤ Cut out the nets of the prisms carefully and make the number rollers.

✤ Roll the two rollers and enter the number on to your calculator.

✤ Roll the two rollers again, and add this number to the one already on your calculator.

✤ Record the result.

✤ Do this ten times. What are your highest and lowest scores?

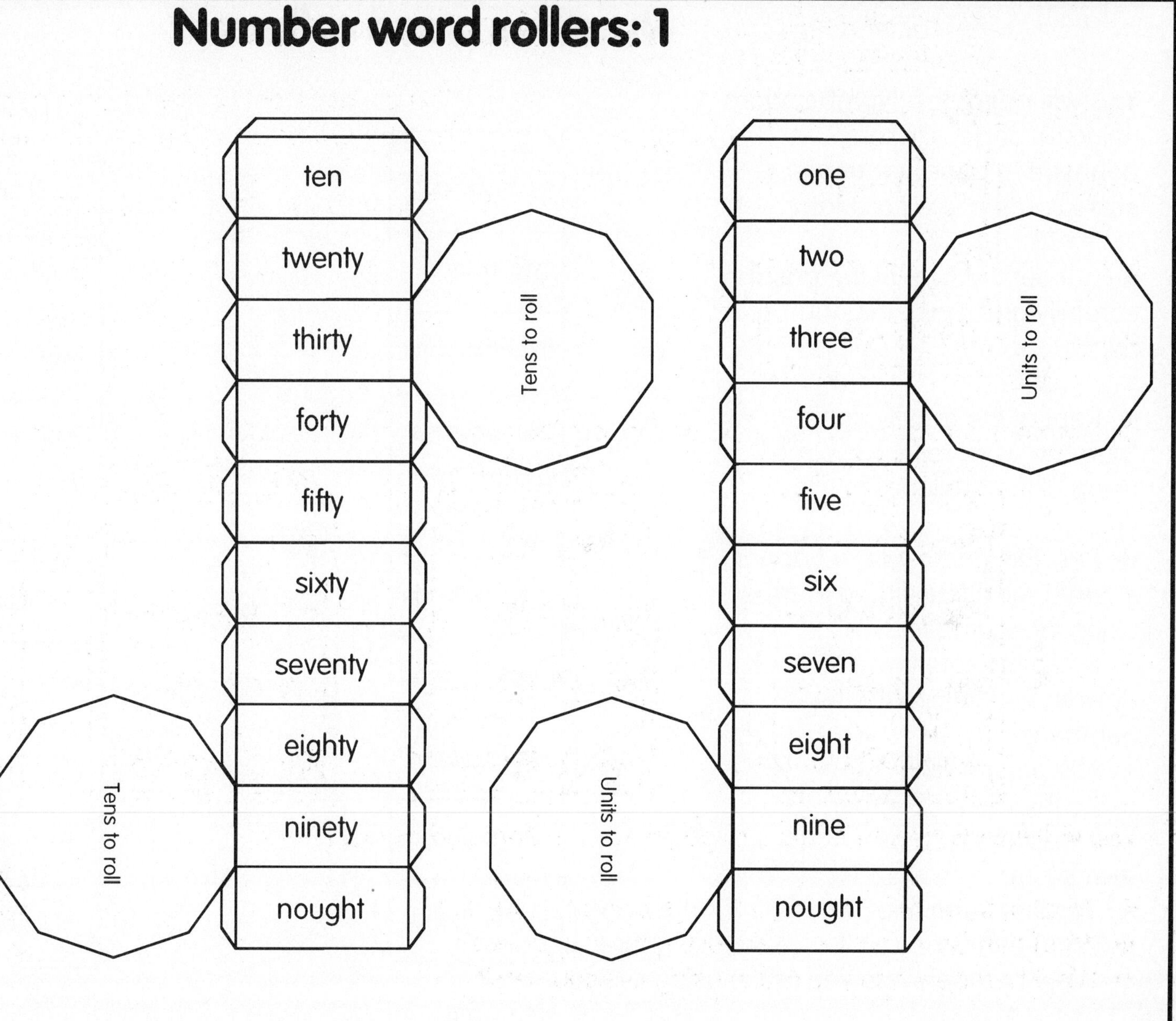

Name ____________________

Number word rollers: 2

Number word rollers: 2

You will need: the 'Number word rollers: 1' page, scissors, adhesive, a pencil, paper for score cards and a calculator.

✤ Cut out the nets of the prisms carefully and make the number rollers.

✤ Repeat the activity on the 'Number word rollers: 1' page using all four rollers.

✤ Play this game with a partner.
- Both roll a four-figure number using the four rollers.
- Both calculate the difference between the two numbers.
- The person who rolled the higher number has the difference as their score.
- The first person to reach 10 000 wins.

one thousand
two thousand
three thousand
four thousand
five thousand
six thousand
seven thousand
eight thousand
nine thousand
ten thousand

Thousands to roll

Thousands to roll

one hundred
two hundred
three hundred
four hundred
five hundred
six hundred
seven hundred
eight hundred
nine hundred
nought

Hundreds to roll

Hundreds to roll

Exploring the multiplication grid

You will need: the multiplication grid, a pencil, paper and a calculator.

✤ Look at the numbers on the multiplication grid in the columns below the 3 and the 5. Find the difference between each pair. Continue the pattern.
For example:

3	5	Difference = 2
6	10	Difference = 4
9	15	Difference = 6

✤ Try this with the numbers under the 4 and 6, and the 7 and 9. Write down what you have found out.

✤ Repeat this with the numbers under the 4 and 7, the 6 and 8, and the 11 and 14.

✤ Find some other columns which give the same result. Write down what you have found out.

✤ Try some other pairs of numbers.

✤ When will you get a difference of 36? In how many ways can you do this?

✤ When will you get a difference of 45? In how many ways can you do this?

Name ____________

The 4 × 4 magic square

In a magic square the numbers in any row add up to the same number as the numbers in any column or the numbers on any diagonal.
For example, in a 3 × 3 magic square:

2	7	6	→ 15
9	5	1	
4	3	8	
↓ 15		↘ 15	

✤ Use your calculator to find the missing numbers in the square below so that it is a magic square.

16	3	2	
	10	11	8
9	6		12
4	15	14	1

These two squares are not quite magic.

✤ Correct some of the numbers so that they become magic.

77	12	2	62
22	27	53	37
42	27	32	56
17	72	67	2

176	35	23	144
56	101	122	89
100	67	78	133
45	166	155	12

Name ____________________

Duplation

Duplation is really about doubling. It is sometimes called the 'Egyptian method' because examples of this type of calculation were found in an Ancient Egyptian document, the Rhind Papyrus.

One way of doing 11 × 23 is to start doubling the larger number and then add up parts of the doubling. To double 23, use 2 × × 23 = = = = = . Enter the results on a table like this:

1	23
2	46
4	92
8	184
16	368
32	736

From the left-hand column in the table, choose numbers that add up to 11, such as 8 + 2 + 1. Then 11 × 23 = 184 + 46 + 23 = 253. If you check on your calculator you should find that this is correct.

To do 37 × 23: 37 = 32 + 4 + 1, so 37 × 23 = 736 + 92 + 23 = 851. Check this result on your calculator.

✤ Use this method to calculate 17 × 23, 15 × 23, 23 × 23, and 19 × 23.

✤ Use duplation to do the following calculations. Use your calculator to check your results.

7 × 22	6 × 24	3 × 28	5 × 37	9 × 41	11 × 123
9 × 22	8 × 24	5 × 28	7 × 37	11 × 41	13 × 123
11 × 22	11 × 24	9 × 28	12 × 37	21 × 41	19 × 123
13 × 22	12 × 24	10 × 28	16 × 37	30 × 41	21 × 123
14 × 22	19 × 24	13 × 28	21 × 37	36 × 41	25 × 123
15 × 22	24 × 24	28 × 28	25 × 37	40 × 41	30 × 123
21 × 22	29 × 24	33 × 28	37 × 37	41 × 41	32 × 123

Name ________________

Digital paper

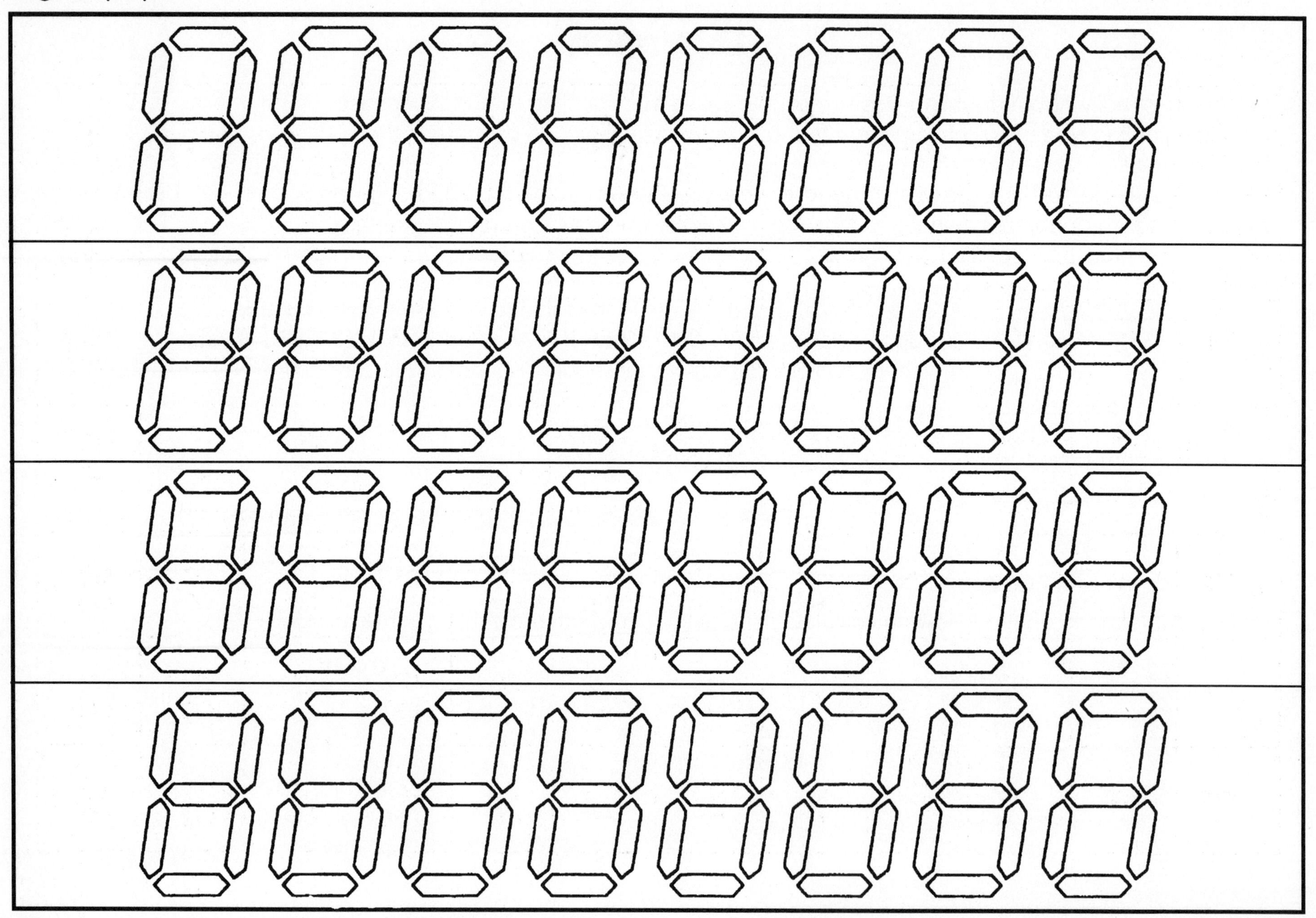

Name ____________________

3 and 4 number grids

1	2	3	4
5	6	7	8
9	10	11	12
13	14	15	16
17	18	19	20
21	22	23	24
25	26	27	28
29	30	31	32
33	34	35	36
37	38	39	40
41	42	43	44
45	46	47	48

1	2	3
4	5	6
7	8	9
10	11	12
13	14	15
16	17	18
19	20	21
22	23	24
25	26	27
28	29	30
31	32	33
34	35	36

Name ____________________

6 number grid

1	2	3	4	5	6
7	8	9	10	11	12
13	14	15	16	17	18
19	20	21	22	23	24
25	26	27	28	29	30
31	32	33	34	35	36
37	38	39	40	41	42
43	44	45	46	47	48
49	50	51	52	53	54
55	56	57	58	59	60
61	62	63	64	65	66
67	68	69	70	71	72

Name ____________________

10 number grid

1	2	3	4	5	6	7	8	9	10
11	12	13	14	15	16	17	18	19	20
21	22	23	24	25	26	27	28	29	30
31	32	33	34	35	36	37	38	39	40
41	42	43	44	45	46	47	48	49	50
51	52	53	54	55	56	57	58	59	60
61	62	63	64	65	66	67	68	69	70

Name ______________

0 to 17 number cards

0	1	2	3	4	5
6	7	8	9	10	11
12	13	14	15	16	17

Name ______________________

Pocket money toy cards

a plastic fly 17p	ball 45p	small teddy 99p	spinning top 12p
engine 75p	yo-yo 35p	badge 30p	doll 97p
pencil with novelty top 14p	polystyrene glider 33p	Tyrannosaurus 49p	pack of marbles 99p

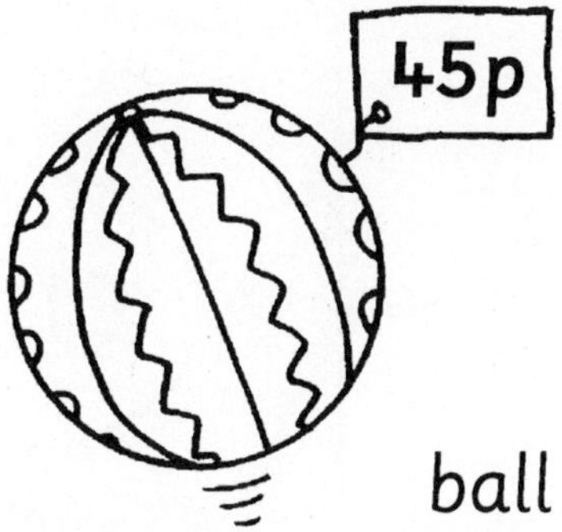

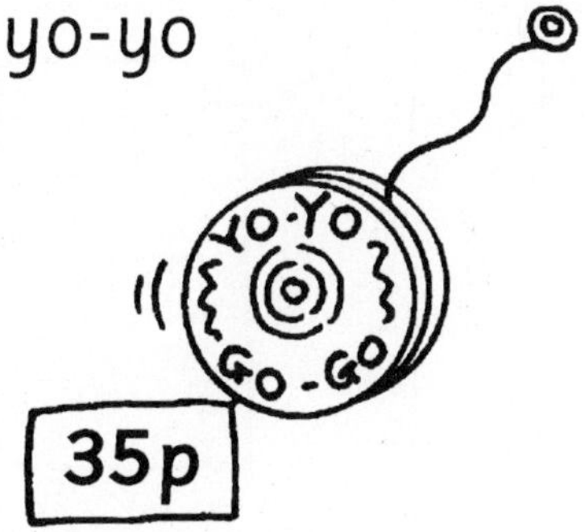

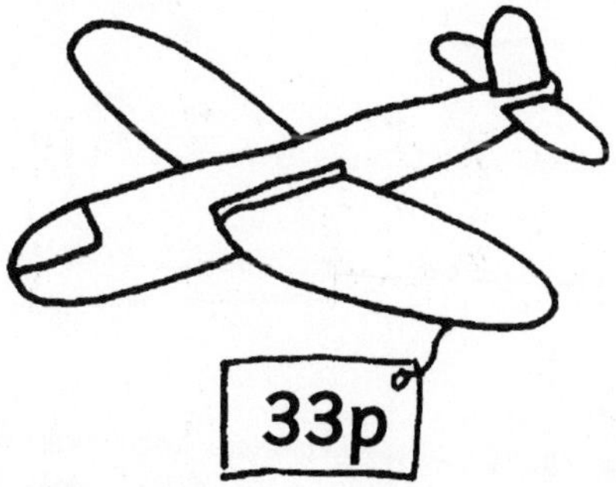

Name ____________

Price label cards

£1.99 **Card 1**	£3.76 **Card 2**	39p **Card 3**	£1.25 **Card 4**	£1.46 **Card 5**
£1.89 **Card 6**	75p **Card 7**	£2.69 **Card 8**	79p **Card 9**	£1.19 **Card 10**
89p **Card 11**	£4.49 **Card 12**	£2.75 **Card 13**	99p **Card 14**	49p **Card 15**

Name ______________________

Multiplication grid

×	1	2	3	4	5	6	7	8	9	10	11	12	13	14	15	16	17	18	19	20	21
1	1	2	3	4	5	6	7	8	9	10	11	12	13	14	15	16	17	18	19	20	21
2	2	4	6	8	10	12	14	16	18	20	22	24	26	28	30	32	34	36	38	40	42
3	3	6	9	12	15	18	21	24	27	30	33	36	39	42	45	48	51	54	57	60	63
4	4	8	12	16	20	24	28	32	36	40	44	48	52	56	60	64	68	72	76	80	84
5	5	10	15	20	25	30	35	40	45	50	55	60	65	70	75	80	85	90	95	100	105
6	6	12	18	24	30	36	42	48	54	60	66	72	78	84	90	96	102	108	114	120	126
7	7	14	21	28	35	42	49	56	63	70	77	84	91	98	105	112	119	126	133	140	147
8	8	16	24	32	40	48	56	64	72	80	88	96	104	112	120	128	136	144	152	160	168
9	9	18	27	36	45	54	63	72	81	90	99	108	117	126	135	144	153	162	171	180	189
10	10	20	30	40	50	60	70	80	90	100	110	120	130	140	150	160	170	180	190	200	210
11	11	22	33	44	55	66	77	88	99	110	121	132	143	154	165	176	187	198	209	220	231

Name ___________________

The line abacus

First number	Second number	Result
Thousands		
Five hundreds Hundreds		
Fifties Tens		
Fives Units		